THE SECRET DIARY OF MONSIEUR CANTONA
Charles Bogle

First published in 1996 by
Juma
Trafalgar Works
44 Wellington Street
Sheffield S1 4HD
Tel. 0114 272 0915
Fax. 0114 278 6550

ISBN 1 872204 20 1?

The Secret Diary of Monsieur Cantona (November 1992-April 1996)
previously appeared in the first ever Man United fanzine, RED NEWS.

The right of RED NEWS to be identified as the author of this work has
been asserted in accordance with the Copyright, Designs and Patents
Act 1988.

You can read the Secret Diary of Monsieur Cantona in every issue
of RED NEWS, THE Utd fanzine! A three issue subscription to RED
NEWS (all-inclusive) costs just £4 in the UK & £5.50 for outside the
UK. Please make all sterling cheques/Postal Orders/International
Money Orders payable to RED NEWS.

RED NEWS, P.O.Box 384, London, WC1 N 3RJ. (0171-404-6042)

PREFACE

This spoof diary was transcribed from the original sanskrit by Charles Bogle - or Chazza as he's not known to his friends. The author would like to apologise to anyone with an unusually long nose and an unusually thin skin. After all, long noses have never stopped anyone playing top-class football. This book is dedicated to all those people in life who tell you: 'Don't worry, there's always someone worse off than yourself'. Just look at any follower of Man City.

Anyway, thanks awfully, ta so much sweeties and the usual luvvies acknowledgements go to Madame Karen Bogle for keeping a straight face at bad jokes, to bebe Bogle for all the fun, and bebe Bogle to be. To Mr Barney C the big cheese, to Martin Lacey for the backing and to Des Buckley for his great illustrations. And, finally, thanks to Sergeant Wilkinson for making it all possible.

CB 1996

'Soup and fish explain half the emotions of life'

Sydney Smith (1771-1845)

'When ze seagulls follow ze trawler it is because zey think sardines will be thrown into ze sea'

Eric Cantona (1966-)

INTRODUCTION

Diaries are very strange things, in which people record their strangest thoughts. My Aunt Vanessa, unbeknown to the rest of our family, kept one for the last seventy years of her life, in which she recorded the time and volume of each nose pick. She also sellotaped prize examples to each page. It's a sick world.

For the last four years Red News, the first ever Man. Utd. fanzine, has been publishing a diary equally full of rich pickings. This time, though, it is the secret diary of Monsieur Cantona - which was first published in Red News long before he earned cult status.

I looked up 'secret' in the Chambers Dictionary and one of the definitions was: 'Private, as in external sexual organs'. I hope this helps.

Four years ago when I sat drinking a pint of Guinness in a pub in Weatherfield, an old man in a raincoat that smelled of wee came in offering goods for sale. "Two old Timex watches", or "Star Wars toy figures" or "some mad secret diary of a French geezer".

I offered him a packet of dry roasted peanuts for the diary and was transfixed. Here was life in all its rich and smelly detail. I passed the secret diary on to Red News and they have been printing it every issue since.

The old derelict has only ever said that he finds it in a skip: "In a posh district with fragments of rabbit pie". For four years now I've been glued to the installments of the Secret Diary of Monsieur Cantona - the outrageous and ludicrous outpourings of an obviously strange mind. But what hilarity! Some of Britain's great comic characters - from Alan Ballsup to Graeme Le sick - are lampooned in this silly, silly book.

We hope you enjoy this publication which will delight any football fan who likes the irreverent side of the game. But anyone of a sensitive disposition should be warned. Chundering, urine, excrement, pillage, badly taken throw-ins and Brian McLard's enormous stomach are All there.

As some bloke called Joe once said: "With madness, as with vomit, it is often the passer-by who is inconvenienced". Read on!

1992

SATURDAY 28TH NOVEMBER

I avv decided to keep a secret diary and will start with my first United match. I watched from the stand at Arse-nil with Bobby Charlton. He wore a hand-crafted blue beret that looked very Parisian. I said to him, 'Bobby, in France, a bald man exposes his crown to the world and he is proud to be known as 'an onion dome'. He scowled at me. Maybe Bobby is very touchy about his hair - both of them. Tony Adams was eating a carrot in the players' lounge - I wonder if this is why he is known as Donkey?

SUNDAY 6TH DECEMBER

A big day for moi...my first game for ze Reds. I am beginning to see the differences between my new manager and Howard's End. The papers avv said zat I fell out with Sergeant Wilko, but ze truth is that I found his little notebook one day and he had a fit when he saw me laughing. 'But Sergeant Wilko' I said, 'Why do you write dirty limericks during the match...and why do you keep sketching David Batty's buttocks?'. We did not speak again. I have not yet solved the mystery of Monsieur Fergie's character. All I have decided so far is that he must have a poor diet as he keeps going very red in the face! The match was a trifle dull. There was a strange man playing for them. He was slow, dirty and balding and the other players kept calling him a 'Macca'. I thought this meant one of those sad old bastards in the park who flash their tackle at little girls and boys. Choccy said, 'Yeah, that's right'.

SATURDAY 12TH DECEMBER

We beat Norwich 1-0 and the man called Kiddo wet himself.

MONDAY 21ST DECEMBER

On Saturday I scored my first goal for United, at Stamford Bridge. On my way to training today I bumped into a funny little man who said he was Danny Wallace. He said zat I was a freak. He reckoned that it took a player 10 years to settle at Old Trafford. He also moaned that it was my nickname zat gave me an unfair advantage. He sang 'Ooh, Ahh, Cantona!' and then said: 'See mate. I mean, what the fuck can you sing to Danny Wallace?' I was going to suggest 'Ohh Danny, shake your fanny!' but he had already pulled a hamstring.

Sadly for him he cannot get treatment because Bryan Robson has been on the treatment table for so long that he has become welded to it.

MONDAY 28TH DECEMBER
Today we thrashed Coventry 5-0 and I was so appy with the game zat I decided to speak to my team-mates. I started to tell Paul Incy-Wincy about my love of Rimbaud, but he broke my heart by saying 'Yeah mate, great films, bloody great that Stallone bloke'. I have come to ze conclusion that all footballers are the same. They all make love to Lionel Ritchie records (except some at Elland Road who used to go off dressed in big Wellington boots with tapes of Ba, Ba Black Sheep...zis I could not fathom out).

1993

TUESDAY 5TH JANUARY
I avv a duty to enlighten my colleagues. I took in my copy of poet Rimbaud's book 'A Season In Hell', but when Brucey said: 'Is that Neil Webb's new book?' everyone laughed.

SATURDAY 9TH JANUARY
We beat Spurs and I scored again. I am not sure if Monsieur Fergie was angry or appy, as I could not understand him.

SUNDAY 10TH JANUARY
I am worried. All the players call Denis Irwin 'Bogman'. I avv decided to avoid going to the urinals with him until I have found out how he earned zat name.

MONDAY 11TH JANUARY
Zat funny little man Danny Wallace came up to me today and said: 'What do you get if you cross a sandwich with a famous Parisian cathedral?' I told him zat I did not know the answer and he shouted: 'The lunchpack of Notre Dame'. I called him a little baguette and he started to run away but pulled a hamstring as he did. I went to Monsieur Fergie and said I was worried that I had damaged the team's hopes by causing the injury of a player... 'Danny who?' was all he said.

WEDNESDAY 20TH JANUARY

I cannot stand it much more. Zat Wallace chap ran past me again and yelled "An oeuf is an oeuf!"

WEDNESDAY 27TH JANUARY

I avv seen my first Fergie Fury. It happened when we went in at half-time in the game against Nottingham Forest. He went as red as a beetroot and started talking like Rab Nesbitt. On ze way back onto the pitch I asked Sparky what he had said but Sparky said that when the gaffer starts screaming like that all the players hum the theme tune of 'Hitler has only got one ball' until he has collapsed with exhaustion.

SATURDAY 6TH FEBRUARY

I scored the winner against Sheff Utd. The Bogman said 'Let's have a good crack tonight'... I fled for my life. He should have stayed at Elland Road with zat sort of attitude.

MONDAY 8TH FEBRUARY

All ze players are talking of the affair of a footballer and a Coronation Street star. My translator got it all wrong and told me that Mavis Riley was bonking John Fashanu, but Paul Nosey Parker, who watches all the soaps, said it was the landlady and Fash Ze Bash. They all seem to have these nicknames. We drew 0-0 with Leeds. All our fans kept shouting 'Scum!' at Leeds, and I think this is what is known in England as high praise. I must go. I want to paint the Manchester canal.

TUESDAY 9TH MARCH

We are now within spitting distance of ze title!

SUNDAY 14TH MARCH

Mon Depardieu!!! What a dream I ad last night. I voz being chased up and down ze Eiffel Tower by a gangly striker who voz singing out: "Cuck, cuck, cuck, cuckoldbility...that's the beauty of Ash!". Ven I told this to Choccy, he said that cuckold came from ze old French word cukeweld, an allusion to the parasitic cuckoos zat lay their eggs in the nests of other birds. Ouef! "Eggs-actly!" said zat little imp Danny Wallace, who was wearing overalls for some reason and sweeping ze floor.

THURSDAY 25TH MARCH

Danny the Dwarf has made a spectacular change - he has left behind his days as a Premier League reserve...and gone to be the forgotten man of a Division One side. Now zat's what I call a career move!

FRIDAY 26TH MARCH

Ohh no! I avv heard even more strange rumours about ze Bogman's habits. Today he tapped my shoulder while we were showering and said: " How about a game of craps?".

TUESDAY 30TH MARCH

Ohh no again! What an embarrassing moments. I waz just getting changed for training when Incy came up and said: "Ere, Eric. My missus says I should be more sensitive. Nah you're into that Rambo poetry lark - and you being a Parisian and all...".
'Spit it out', I said.
"Ere, I'll get straight to the point. I've done her indoors a poem - go orn, tell us what you reckon". He had written it on ze back of a William Hill betting slip. My face must av flushed as I read it:

'*I crave you darling, my love is hot,*
That's the truth, it ain't just rot,
No message gal,
I'd come to you like a shot.
As Robbo says,
 'It's shit or get off the pot'.

I voz stunned. "You av about as much talent as Kafka's dick!" I told him, but to my amazement he just said: "Cheers Eric, I thought you'd like it". I think English footballers should just stick to ze Questions of Sport.

THURSDAY 1ST APRIL

Sparky came up with a magnifique April Fools' Day jape. He crept into Clayton's little private gym. Clayton, as usual, was asleep on ze sunbed, listening to KC and the Sunshine Band on his little Sony Walkman. Sparky covered his face with a droopy banana. When Clayton appeared he had a big penis-shaped white mark on his tanned face. He voz hopping mad, shouting: "That's it - I can't take part in any televised games now!". Somehow, ze lads did not feel this would be too much of a problem.

SUNDAY 4TH APRIL

Ze squad reported to Cliff's training ground for ze trip to Norwich. Fergie decided to ban ze papers, because he had seen a headline about 'Fat Fergie on the scrounge', but it turned out to be ze royal Fergie. All ze lads were incensed at the Grand National disgrace. What a grand English cock up. Only ze English could leave an important event like zat to be run by old codgers in bowler hats. "Well what the fuck would the Frogs av done about it mate?" asked Les Sell-by-date in zat chirpy little Cock-er-knee way of his. "We would have shot ze old fart with the flag and made beef bourguignon out of the winning horse", I said. When someone said Kiddo was a horse's arse he wet himself again.

MONDAY 5TH APRIL

We went in happy at half-time, after having made onion soup of ze piddly little Canaries. Brucey Bonus said: 'If only we had Neil Webb to give us that extra bit of pace' and I swear even Fergie laughed. His face takes on a whole new character when he is not screaming abuse at us.

WEDNESDAY 7TH APRIL

Ze lads are annoyed because Annie Walker, ze boss of the Canaries, has said we were not ze best team they have played zis season. In the Dordoigne zis would be known as ze sour grapes.

ZE GOOD FRIDAY, 9TH APRIL

I av not made much mention of recent matches. But once I av played in zem I forget them. Pally says he watches zem over and over on ze satellite TV. He says that ze Dutch Reds station plays ze best action shots of all. I av so far not written about ze terrible accusation zat I crapped on ze head of a Leeds fan. Zis set up a terrible storm, ze like of which I av not seen since Fergie sat on my extra runny Camembert in his new shell suit. Anyways, ze Leeds fans said zat it was outrageous zat I should single out one fan and zat if there was any free crap floating about they were all entitled to some. Must go! I want to watch ze Spitting Image and drink a big goblet of wine...

SATURDAY 10TH APRIL

Great balls of Sacha Distel!! What a match today. Steve Brucey Bonus used his loaf of bread/head, as Incy put it, to win at ze death of ze game against Sheffield Tuesday. Ze man called Kiddo excelled himself...he wet his pants in front of 40,000 people!

MONDAY 12TH APRIL

Ohh no! A bad day for ze world of art. I av hurt my wristy-pooh in ze game against Coventry and cannot now paint a picture of Martin Deadwoods's lady friend. Ze Bogman scored a great goal and said after zat he was pleased to have got it out of his system. I think ze answer to his personality lies in ze potty training period. All ze lads were ranting about an aggressive pot-bellied wanker in a blue shirt. But Incy must have been a big fan - he had taken a great clump of his greasy hair as a souvenir.

FRIDAY 16TH APRIL

I voz accosted by a Leeds United fan, who accused me of being a traitor. "Eee by gum, Eric, why did thou leave t'best team in the league?'. "But I joined zem, you ugly little meat ball" I replied. But before I could say anything else, his ferret escaped and bit him on ze arse.

SATURDAY 27TH APRIL

Another great day at Old Trafford. I scored a magnifique goal and knocked over two pansies to do it. I thought it was nice of ze Chelsea team to allow zat Dave Beasant to av a chance in goal. It is good of zese clubs to allow people with handling difficulties to av a job. A jolly man called Tommy Docherty was in the bar after ze game and he told everyone zat Beasant had put an ansaphone in ze goalmouth with ze message: "Sorry I'm not here at the moment".

WEDNESDAY 21ST APRIL

Tonight we beat Pisspoor Palace 2-0. Sparky bagged a great volley from my cross. After ze game Alex ze Gaffer voz going around wiv such a big grin zat we thought he must have taken a cigarette of ze wacky-backy!

MONDAY 3RD MAY

Are you reading Big Fat Ron? Zat oaf who made ze comments about ze French can eat his own baguette. United are ze Champions!! It has been a great six months! Glory Glory Man United!

MONDAY 24TH MAY

Ooh la la. Today it is mon anniversaire. Zat is my 27th birthday to ze non French speaking people. I avv been to visit my great-great granny, who lives in a petit village called Ville-fucked-upzereti-tlechances. We add some apple gateux and champagne to celebrate ze title win.

SUNDAY 6TH JUNE

I was chosen by ze famous French designer, Rabanne, to strut up ze catwalk wearing some of ze famous new ranges of ze clothes for ze natty folk. Zis means zat ze Bogman, who usually just wears an old tweed waistcoat and sandals, will not be buying any of ze double-breasted suits Rabanne sells. Ze people zere all shouted out: "Ooh Ahh" as I walked down. I avv only a little bit of ze holiday left but I avv to go and do ze signing sessions for a video.

THURSDAY 10TH JUNE

I was signing ze video when a nasty little turd of a man came up and said zat he collected all ze obscure videos - Arsenal's 100 Greatest Backpasses; Steve Nicol, How I built A Career On Taking Throw-Ins. I told him to smell his own farts and get out of ma way.

SATURDAY 3RD JULY

Back to Manchester for a day of painting. Today I did ze bald 'edd' of Bobby Charlton. When you look at it for six hours at a time, it really does begin to look like ze Planet Jupiter. I must ask Brian McLard about zis as he reads ze books on mysteries of ze universe.

SATURDAY 31ST JULY

All ze lads are talking of ze strange case of a little Welshman called Take The Mickey Out Of His John Thomas. Zis little man was passing ze strange £10 notes wiv a picture of Reg Holdsworth where ze Queen's head should be. I think I will check my money very carefully before I play in ze coach card school again.

FRIDAY 6TH AUGUST

We are preparing for ze Charity Shield and SACRE BLUE!!!! Ze lads are amazed by ze news that ze readers of ze Women On Top magazine avv found Gary Pally to be ze footballer zat most women would like to go out with. Not if zey all knew about his smelly feet and his love of cold carrot soup zey would not said Robbo. It was even more startling as the man who got most irate about it was ze Bogman, who said zat he used to take girls in his native Ireland to see municipal toilets on zere first date. I think he should avv had a longer holiday.

1993   *13*

SATURDAY 7TH AUGUST

Ze Charity Shield game went OK, but zat Tony Adams is hard to play against. All 90 minutes he kept chewing and chomping. Ze sound of him stuffing carrots in his gob really is a most distracting one.

SUNDAY 15TH AUGUST

Ze lads got off to a fine start by beating ze Budgies, or whatever zey are, 2-0. Robbo, who has been eating packet after packet of ze Sanatogen Feel Zippy When You're An Oldie pills, played like a trooper. It is amazing but he is old enough to be Giggsy's father. Mon Dieu.

WEDNESDAY 18TH AUGUST

I avv a hamstring injury so did not play in ze victory against ze Sheffield United team. Ze lads were all teasing me, asking if I got ze injury getting my leg over - but zey know zat I got it kicking Clayton in ze head for what he did to Giggsy.

FRIDAY 20TH AUGUST

Today we got invited to a Liverpool players' party but we all turned it down. After reading all zat stuff in ze News Of Ze Screws we knew what it would be like. When I first arrived in England I thought ze people were joking when zey talked of ze Liverpool players, but zere it was in ze black and white - some of zem think zere idea of fun is to drink a glass of urine. Zat is taking ze piss.

SATURDAY 21ST AUGUST

Manchester was engulfed by all zose odd balls with tatooes zat say things like 'Away Mam You Big Slag' all over zere backs. Ze players all had their minds on ze latest excuse zat Lee NotsoSharpe came up with for his black eyes zat we could not concentrate and drew 1-1. Sharpeypooh said zat he got ze eyes black when a boiled egg fell out of a tree house and smashed him on ze bridge of the nose. Zat boy is spaced out, man!

MONDAY 23RD AUGUST

I avv just got back from ze France match with ze Swedes. I do not like zem. Zey come over here with their pine funiture...Great balls of Sacha Distel! I went to see ze lads at Villa Park. Zey were magnifique in winning 2-1 and afterwards zat Fat Ron was so angry zat I thought he was going to choke on three Big Macs he was cramming into his face. I cannot wait for my first league match. Zere is no doubt about it - things are going to be hot this season.

SATURDAY 28TH AUGUST

Zut alors! I scored a cracker of a goal at ze Dell, a delicate brush-like chip (I love ze arty phrases) but vot a weird place to play at zat ground is. All ze carrot-crunchers are right up against ze pitch talking about zere crop harvests during ze game. On ze coach back all ze lads were taking ze pissoir out of Paul Nosey Parker for listening to his Michael Jackson tapes. "What chocolate does Wacko Jacko have when he's finished a meal?" said Sparky. "Answer - an Under Eight". We all laughed at zat and Parker put on his Best of Woody Allen instead.

THURSDAY 2ND SEPTEMBER

We beat ze Hammers yesterday night and I scored a nifty little penalty. Sharpey scored with a header and zat mad boy nearly knocked me out of ze way to get to ze ball. Zat boy is always going on about his boogie nights out and we avv add a big mirror put in ze dressing room so he can do his shuffles before ze games. After ze game a sweaty fat Yorkshireman came up to me and said: "Ere, Canty mate. Zat were a reet good show you put on. I think you're really it!". I tapped him on ze arm and said: "Well, now you're it", but he add one of zose stupid hang-dog faces and he definitely did not get ze joke.

SUNDAY 12TH SEPTEMBER

I woke up with a sore ankle. Zere were little bite marks around my ankle - it must be zat little turd Dennis UnWise. All ze Sunday papers were full of my after-match comments. I said zat Glenn Hoddle was like Mozart whereas most English players are like hard rock musicians. I could have taken zese descriptions further, because Danny Wallace is about as entertaining as Val Doonican (it always make me laugh when I think zat he must avv ze initials VD on his person-alised towels), but I must stop taking ze pissior out of little Danny because I fear he is not long for zis club.

THURSDAY 16TH SEPTEMBER

We avv just flown back from Hungary after beating ze little Honved. I saw my little brother over zere. Ze United players kept coming up and saying zat we looked so alike: "How come, though...", said Clayton Blackhead, "Zat you have not got ze same bandage?". I think zat man must avv fallen hard on his head when he was a baby.

Zere were a load of crappy reports in ze Daily Porn (sorry, Daily Star) zat ze Hungarians were going to chuck golf balls filled with explosives. In fact zey kept spitting bits of old walnuts at us, but zis did not get in ze papers.

SATURDAY 18TH SEPTEMBER

Ze gaffer (I adore zese footballing phrases) was getting us prepared to face ze Gunners and he was trying to be all philosophical but he was being a bit confusing: "A man who is tired of Manchester United is a man who is in need of a good night's sleep" he said. Still at least he was not avving one of his tantrums. I avv asked him if I can paint him when he is avving a Fergie fury because if I painted his face I could use up zat big tube of maroon paint zat I still avv.

SUNDAY 19TH SEPTEMBER

We beat ze Gunners and I scored with a humdinger of a free kick. I still cannot get used to playing against Tony Adams. He makes all zese odd braying sounds during ze game...and I swear it looks like he has a tail coming out of his shorts. Ze lads all agreed zat Arse-nil don't look like Championship material. For a start zere formation of 8-1-1 meant zat zey only get ze ball as far as ze half-way line. Zere manager George Graham was not a happy soul after ze game.

SATURDAY 26TH SEPTEMBER

I missed ze midweek game against Stoke. Dion Belfast scored. Zis was big news to me, because I had always assumed zat he was ze boy who worked in ze ticket office. But no! He was bought for one million pounds! Sacre Bleu! Today we beat Swindle Town, who were pissoir poor. I scored again and it was like shelling corn on ze cob.

TUESDAY 28TH SEPTEMBER

Great balls of Sacha Distel! I had beaucoup de problems last night when I went out to a little bistro and a mangy little Manchester Shitty fan came up to me and started moaning away. "The only reason City aren't doing well is because of a CIA plot. By appointing Peter Swales they accomplished the following: making Man City into a second-rate team and allowing you Reds to dominate the city...it's not fair". He would have prattled on like zat for hours, but I told him zat like so many of life's born failures he had become a Man City fan. Zen I poured my asparagus soup down his trousers and rammed a chocolate croisant up his nostrils. It is ze only way to deal with zese turds.

WEDNESDAY 29TH SEPTEMBER

We are through to ze next round of ze European Cup. In truth, zough, it was a boring game against Honved. After ze game we all went to Robbo's house for a drinkypoo. "Let me tell you all about ze poetry of Rimbaud" I told Incy, but he said: "Just pour me a lager you French twit!". Sometimes zat lad gets above his station.

FRIDAY 1ST OCTOBER

Ze lads avv a new competition...Spot ze products zat Giggsy is endorsing. So far we avv ze Reebok pumps, Ralph Lauren clothes and Granny Leek's Old Welsh Cock ALeekie Soup. Still, Giggsy took ze jibes in good spirit and we all agreed zat Sharpey spends most of his nights on Planet Reebok.

SATURDAY 2ND OCTOBER

We avv been having a laugh at ze Mandy Smith book which Bogman has bought. Robbo told him zat zere was a picture in it of Bill Wyman's lavatory so ze Bogman was all upset when he could not find it. Clayton Blackhead boasted zat he had add Mandy, but ze only Smith he has add is a pint of John's. Brucey Bonus grabbed ze book and started reading aloud ze bit where she says zat Pat Van Den Hauwe (ze 'world-class' player according to Hello) scribbles notes to her in lipstick on ze bed sheets! "I bet zat's his own lipstick"...ve all laughed hard at zat. Oh yes, and we beat ze Owls 3-2. Sparky did a neat little dummy to beat Chris Flapper Woods and ze man Kiddo wet himself, which has not happened for three days.

FRIDAY 15TH OCTOBER

We are all totally pissoired-off. Graham Failure fucked up ze England World Cup chances and France are in a bit of trouble after losing to Israel. Danny Wallace ran into ze dressing room and said: "I'm going to have the last laugh on the lot of you - I have signed for the biggest club between Walsall and Coventry! Just you wait I'll be an England regular in a year's time". We were all stunned but as he opened his car door to leave we heard his hamstring go again. It will not be ze same without little Danny here - who will wash my bandage for me now?

TUESDAY 19TH OCTOBER

Seven points clear now, but zere was one Spurs player who is dirty. He kept threatening me, so I told him: "If you hurt my armsie-warmsie, I'll stamp on your footsie-wootsie!". Zere is nothing like poetry in action! Ze lads were having a sweepstake on what is really under my bandage. We all add a big shock when we left ze training ground. A woman outside calling herself Pauline the Poll Tax Woman was defecating on the pavement and shouting: "Kiddo loves me". Apparently she is well known for her lunacy and so plump and ugly zat even Brother Blackhead would not desire her. Ah well, roast Turkey tommorow!

WEDNESDAY 20TH OCTOBER
Tonight we fucked up against ze Turks. I am too upset to write ze diary any more tonight.

SATURDAY 23RD OCTOBER
We beat Everton 1-0 and on ze journey home I told ze lads about ze famous French psychotherapist Emile Coue, who said: "Every day in every way I am getting better and better". Zen Brucey Bonus said: "I think Webb heard that advice - only someone told him it was fatter and fatter". All ze lads laughed and zen for some strange reason they began singing: "Webb ate all the pies!". Sacre Bleu!

SATURDAY 30TH OCTOBER
I can detect a big change in Paul Incey-Wincey. No longer is he ze frail flower of ze Eastenders ghetto. He said he wants to be an in-ter-lectual like. He has bought a book of Victorian phrases and keeps telling me some. "Ere, Eric mate, do you know what the phrase 'He will never shit a seaman's turd' means?".I told him I did not but wondered if it was to do with ze strange players at Arse-nil. 'No mate', he said, it was said by sailors to those who wouldn't make it...Perhaps I was right after all! I scored a delightfully cheeky goal today against Queens in ze Park Rangers.

SUNDAY 31ST OCTOBER
Bossman Fergie had us all in to prepare for ze Turkey trip, but he could not stop eating bananas. Maybe zis is what Robbo meant when he said Fergie goes bananas all ze time.

MONDAY 1ST NOVEMBER
On ze plane to Istanbul all ze lads were cracking jokes and listening to Dire Straits' Sultan of Swing. "Let's talk Turkey" Bogman Denis said as he ate his little bread roll. "Fergie's told me I'm in the team and my job is to stick to their winger like shit to a blanket". Where did ze Bogman learn zese crude phrases?

TUESDAY 2ND NOVEMBER

I don't like Istanbul. All ze men have moustaches - and most of ze women. Zey are so ugly you would sooner go with them zan kiss them goodbye. All ze lads were sympathetic with Giggsy after ze pissoir written about his father in ze tabloids!

WEDNESDAY 3RD NOVEMBER

Great balls of Sacha Distel! What a night! Ze whole ground was full of human castaways, spitting and growling like Terry PhelanAwful at a Christmas party. We were crap-poor but ze Turks kept time-wasting. I was so upset to go out of ze European Cup. At ze end a fat little arsehole in black walked by. I think his name was Kurt Arselicker or something. I was shown ze red card but all I did was make a little circle for him to show how many goals we had scored and zen I said: "Jolly nice to have met you old bean". Zat is ze official version for UEFA ears, but in truth I did happen to tell him zat I hoped a huge vat of liquid shit fell on him, zat his balls developed elephantitus and zat I hoped he was satisfied ze ugly, turf-brained little pipsqueak. On ze way back ze Turkish police laid into me and when good old Robbo turned to help zey hit him with a riot shield. Zese filthy Ottoman arseholes are not even part of Europe! I am not a happy Monsieur tonight.

THURSDAY 3RD NOVEMBER

I am going to be reported to UEFA. Merde to zem, I say. It also turns out zat Paul Nosey Parker was hit and Kiddo had his incontinence sheets confiscated. Zey also attacked our fans in zere hotel beds. Even ze Bogman was not happy. "I thought I'd be able to see ze toilets of the East, but the dirty buggers just shit as they stand up", he said, "...Just like the mules at home in old County Corblimey".

SUNDAY 7TH NOVEMBER

Ze lads were all a little down on ze way to Maine Road until Brucey Bonus told us a story. Apparently when Gazza joined Lazio he was very tubby and Dino Zoff said to him: "Listen here Paul Gascoigne. I know that you are carrying too much weight. We have a game against Juventus. I have included you in the team but what I want you to do is race around for 45 minutes doing as much as you can and then I'll pull you off at half-time". "Wha hay" said Gazza. "All I ever got at Tottenham was a slice of orange!". Ze match against ze Shitty was most enjoyable. Zey were 2-0 up and all zere bitter fans were celebrating as though zey had won ze Cup Final. But all zere joy turned to bitter blue tears in ze second half. I was pleased to score and afterwards I heard Fergie shouting: "So what was zat about a broken down washing machine you stupid little tool". I don't know who he was talking to, but ze man ran off. Ze curious thing was zat ze man left a trial of slime in his wake like he was a slug or something.

SATURDAY 13TH NOVEMBER
It is nice to have a day off. For some reason little Danny Wallace rang me and shouted down ze line: "You all think I'm mutton dressed as lamb, don't you?". I do miss him, he used to make such lovely Eccles cakes in his spare time.

FRIDAY 19TH NOVEMBER
All ze lads re-assembled with ze long faces...all except Andrex Andrei, ze Bogman and Roy Keane As Mustard. Zere are not many of us going to USA 94. Ze Bogman is already raving about having a pee in ze bar at Cheers in Boston. Ze most cheesed off were ze English, but when we discussed Graham Failure, Robbo just had a funny smile on his face.

SATURDAY 20TH NOVEMBER
Ze crazy gang came and went without making zere mark. Zey were playing ze heavy rock music and Vinnie Groans was going round the dressing room floor pretending to be a rottweiler, but zey had all ze bite of my old Granny Cantona. "Toujours perdix partridge mon petite Eric", she used to say to me. "What the fuck does that mean?", said Incy. I told him zat it was the French way of saying zat you can have too much of a good thing. "What a load of shit", he said. I'm not going to show him my Harley-Davison now!

WEDNESDAY 24TH NOVEMBER
Zat was ze most freezing boring game I have seen in my whole year at United. Clayton Blackhead said: "I've seen Lesley Ash's tits in a video, have you seen her tits Eric?". Zat silly Welshman. She only has one tit - and he's called Lee. Boom boom, missus. Eric Cantona's the name, there'll never be another.

FRIDAY 3RD DECEMBER
Tomorrow we play ze Budgies. All ze lads went for a drink at a theme pub after training and we were all talking about ze Work's Christmas Party. Zis is a big thing in England. I told zem zat at Leeds all zey did

was go walking on ze Moors in mackintosh coats, but Streudal said we should have a pantomine. "They'd be allright at Newcastle", said Sparky, "...Beardsley could play the lead in the Hunchback of St James Park". We all laughed. I hope ze idea takes off, although I have my own suspicions about who would want to play ze womens' parts!

SUNDAY 19TH DECEMBER
An enjoyable game against Aston Vanilla. I scored two goals and finally got ze chance to show off my little boogie. I avv got sick of seeing Sharpey do his dance. So I showed my Advertising Board shuffle. I had a strange message on my answerphone when I got home. It was an old lady calling herself Old Ma Culverhouse. "You didn't kick anyone in the balls today, what's wrong?". Zese frustrated English women are a mystery to me.

SATURDAY 25TH DECEMBER
We all watched Only Fools & Horses. Isn't Ron Fatkinson like zis Del Boy?

SUNDAY 26TH DECEMBER
We were all discussing ze Christmas presents before ze game. Christmas is not such a big thing in France but everyone was going mad about it here. Bogman has been given a leopard skin toilet-seat warmer, Mike Phelan some Elton John hair lotion and Darren Ferguson was given an A-Z of Birmingham. What can zis mean? Fergie was in a bit of a state after ze game. He kept saying 'Zat's fucked up Kenny's week!' and chuckling. He was so pleased he forgot to shout at Peter Streudal for going walkabout in ze Rovers penalty box.

WEDNESDAY 29TH DECEMBER
An easy win at Oldham. It was such a stroll zat Fergie even took me off. He looked worried in case I would throw a wobbly but it was such a dull game I didn't mind. On ze coach back Robbo was telling us about how tough Norman Backside used to be. Zen Kiddo said zat Norman had given up trying to be a physio and was training to be a chiropodist. "I bet he has cornflakes for breakfast" said Giggsy. It is ze first joke he has cracked and only Andrex Andrei laughed. And he only understands three words of English - "You greedy sod" I think. Zey are ze ones he hears all ze time from ze rest of us.

FRIDAY 31ST DECEMBER

Ze night before ze game. We were allowed one glass of Old Trafford tawny wine. Clayton Blackhead was acting all big time to one of ze hotel waitresses. Zen Robbo put him down - "Here's Paul Nosey Parker, he's a fullback, here's Bogman, he's a fullback. Here's Clayton, he's a drawback". "Come on" said Brucey Bonus. "Only two things stop Clayton from being a good player". 'What are those' said ze girl. "His feet" said Brucey Bonus. Ve all wet ourselves laughing at zat one. Even Fergie joined in, saying: "Be fair, it's only his third touch that let's him down". Blackhead stomped off leaving his false suntan lotion behind.

1994

SATURDAY 1ST JANUARY

Ze scum came to Old Trafford. Zey had all ze attack momentum of Italian soldiers. I told ze lads that Gordon Stricken's nickname at Elland Road is 'The Green Tongue' because he makes sarcy comments. "I thought it was because he could get it furthest up Wilko's bum" said Sparky.

TUESDAY 4TH JANUARY

Ze journey into Scouseland was like being in one of zose documentaries on ze poor sods who live in rat-infested Shanty towns. Brucey Bonus was teaching me to say "calm down, calm down" in a Scouse accent. We played excellent football for a while. Ze Bogman took a great free kick. "It's shit or bust!" he said before scoring a great goal. Zen we blew it. Ze joke was on us because zey were one of ze worst teams we have played zis season. Neil Fattock is so overweight I think zat he needs liposuction.

SATURDAY 8TH JANUARY

We were staying at a country house before our FA Cup game. Incey had brought his books of Victorian phrases and Bogman was begging him for any about crap or bogs. "Here's one" said Incey. "If someone lent money to all and sundry, then people said ` He would lend his arse and shit through his ribs". Bogman gave a big smile and I swear he began to purr like a cat.

SUNDAY 9TH JANUARY

Zat Sheffield United are a bunch of fuck-pots. Zey have less skill zan one of zose Subbuteo players. Zey had some little mouthy arsehole called Kamikaze in midfield running around saying: "I'll have you. I'll have you too" all ze game. If you ask me he had criminal features to his pug ugly face. Sparky scored a terrific goal and zen he copied my Culverhouse kick and booted someone in the balls. Zere is a knack to it. You must not get sent off. Ze shocking news is zat Bogman has constipation. He has not, as he puts it, "Pumped ship for four days".

SATURDAY 15TH JANUARY

Zat Spurs team are a poor lot. Zere was a funny man with a beard hanging round saying "Anyone need desktop stuff, going cheap". On ze coach home ze lads were telling me of ze latest gossip in ze football world. Who would have thought zat such a well known Tory had slept with Fash ze Queer Bash.

SUNDAY 16TH JANUARY

I avv been told zat George Boring Graham has said some nasty things about me. Zat I am a big cry baby. Zat is rich coming from ze man who would be in anyone's list of Great Old Trafford Flops. Besides, he should be ze patron Saint of Insomniacs. I would not fart on ze Arse-nil team. I think zat when you are sent to purgatory you have to watch un-edited tapes of Arse-nil games and zen listen to George whinge and whine his excuses afterwards. Ze lads thought it was funny. Roy Keane As Mustard said: "Yeah it was really persuasive when George said to me, forget United and their Giggs and Cantona - you could be playing alongside John Jenson and Ray Pizza Parlour".

THURSDAY 20TH JANUARY

Ze sad news broke of ze death of Sir Matt Busby. Zere was no-one here who ever had a bad word to say about him. Now zat would have been a manager to play for.

SATURDAY 22ND JANUARY

Ze emotions were running high when we walked out behind ze Pied Piper - but I thought we put on a good show zat was worthy of ze United legend. I am a happy Monsieur Cantona to be here. I was desperate to score and was so annoyed to see one chance go wide zat I crossed my arms. My wife said she could see I was furious as I only usually do zat when she has done something like tape over Coronation Street on ze video. I avv become a real fan and I see a lot of resemblance between Bet Gilroy and Steve Brucey Bonus. Perhaps it is just ze shape of zere bodies.

SUNDAY 23RD JANUARY

I went to ze pub to watch ze Leeds game. Zere were scummy fans who sang during ze silence for Sir Matt. Zey even had the cheek to sing Don Revie's name. It was funny to see Sergeant Wilko writing in his notebook - it was his first chance to sketch Batty's buttocks for quite a while.

WEDNESDAY 26TH JANUARY

Tonight we beat ze Portsmouth. It was a big relief after all because Bogman revealed he had finally crapped. "What did the trick" asked Pally - "Well I ate 16 tins of prunes and 4 boxes of All Bran". I will not sit next to him on ze coach...

SATURDAY 29TH JANUARY

Everyone has been going on about ze way I keep my collar up during ze games. Ze truth is zat a smelly obese lady called Pauline, who hangs round the toilets at the Cliff, jumped out and gave me a love bite just as I was letting Mister Fireman use his hose. It was so disgusting zat I had to keep it hidden.

SUNDAY 30TH JANUARY

We knocked ze Canaries out of the Cup and zere was a big rumpus because I did a back flick. Zere was some bearded monstrosity calling me names. He must have annoyed ze Boss because Fergie erupted into his Rab C Nesbit character. Ze lads were joking zat it was as dramatic as ze change to a big TV man called Ze Incredible Hulk - only in zis case Fergie goes totally scarlet. We were all silent as he stormed off shouting: "That deformed bollock-brain has gone too far". Funnily enough, though, he had a big grin when he came back from ze press conference saying: "I've just slagged off the world's only living brain donor".

SATURDAY 5TH FEBRUARY

A nice day out at Queens Bend over in ze Park Rangers. Giggsy scored a wonder goal, but zere was a bloke called Wilkins on ze pitch who looked about 70. I think he is older zan Nick Barmby's wife. On ze way back Paul Nosey Parker was telling me about all ze

American soap operas he gets on his Sky dish. His favourite is Baywatch but he denied zis was because he likes looking at the girls' lallies. Giggsy shouted out: "Thanks for the Mamories". I think zat lad has discovered girls.

SUNDAY 13TH FEBRUARY
Already ze postmen are complaining because zey have 9000 Valentine cards for Giggsy. It is funny to see Clayton Blackhead keep coming up and saying all his must have got lost in ze post. It is hardly worth mentioning ze Cup game against Sheffield Tuesday. It was, as Brucey Bonus said, "A bucket of shite".

MONDAY 14TH FEBRUARY
Giggsy ended up with ze most Valentines cards, Lee NotsoSharpe was second and Mike Phelanleftoutofzeteam was third. Zis was suspicious as all ze letters to him had a Burnley post-mark, near where he lives! He was all cheerful for once, saying zat now Robbo is England's No.2 he may win his second cap, "What for United?", said Sparky. Zat was a bit cruel. Some lady called Ivy Tisley sent me a pair of old lips and a biography of Casanova. Zis is a man after my own heart. When he was caught cheating at cards he said he was merely "adjusting ze carelessness of fortune". Fergie pulled me aside and said that, being a Frenchman, I should give some advice to Giggsy on women. I told him zat no wise man ever marries a woman if he can't stand her mother. Giggsy looked puzzled and just said: "That's crucial, dude".

SUNDAY 20TH FEBRUARY
Beat Wimbledon 3-0. Zey are so piss-poor. Vinny Groans tried to play ze hard man but after he was booked he was like a castrated poodle. I scored ze wonder goal of ze month and later Bogman even scored a great goal. He had a huge grin when he came off and said to everyone: "They'll be downing pints tonight in the County Corblimey!". All ze lads were making jokes about John Scales and Britt Eckland. Zere may even be hope for Clayton. Even Dion Belfast got a run out. Ze Boss said to him at half-time, "Oh fuck it, if we go three up you can have a game". Zat was why he was cheering so much when Bogman scored.

FRIDAY 25TH FEBRUARY
Zere was a funny atmosphere at ze pre-match dinner. Ze papers had been full of big talk by all ze backward Eastenders saying zat they

were going to "give Incey grief". My what full lives zese people have. Zey harbour a grudge for all zese years just because a player goes from a little club to ze greatest in Europe. Still Roy Keane As Mustard gave the evening a lighter note when he jumped on ze dinner table, put an orange in his mouth and shouted: "I'm a Tory MP, I'm a Tory MP". I told ze lads zat French politicians were more civilised in zere sexual habits...even in his seventies Mitterand had a young birdie!

SATURDAY 26TH FEBRUARY
Ze lads were all below par. I hurt my leg trying to kick a bread roll at Kiddo in ze morning. Ze Wets Ham fans chucked bananas at Incey. I wonder if this is why zey call ze club The Academy? Is zis what zey call a good old East End knees-up? Still Incey-Wincey had ze last laugh...he was so determined to get to ze ball for ze equaliser. Alvin Stardust is nearly as old as Gay Wilkins...is zere some sort of Premiership Help The Aged campaign group going on?

WEDNESDAY 2ND MARCH
I was out of ze game at Hillsborough, but you wouldn't have noticed. Ze lads were brilliant and Andrex Andrei even managed to pass the ball. Boy oh boy, did it make me regret zat I never joined Sheffield Tuesday.

SATURDAY 5TH MARCH
Sacre Bleu! We lost to a team of dwarfs. I suppose all ze papers will be running zere long-awaited "United will crack" stories. It will make it all ze sweeter to rub zere faces in ze merde as each trophy comes. I know zat Bogman is excited by zis prospect.

MONDAY 7TH MARCH
Sat with a cup of Ribena and watched Giggsy on Question Of Sport. Zat lad was hot. He even got a question right about basketball. But what an arse Beefy Botham was, he thought zat I looked like zat ugly Scouser John Aldridge in ze mystery guest slot. I may have to consult my lawyers.

TUESDAY 8TH MARCH
I am getting ready for ze launch of my big book. It was written with ze help of my interpreter Georgey Porgy Scanlan and Chips. Everyone thinks zat he looks like the Guardian Angel in ze James Stewart film It's A Wonderful Life.

WEDNESDAY 9TH MARCH

Fergie has sent us all a note about ze Chelseasick defeat. "If you turds play that badly again I'll make you watch That's Life videos on every coach trip this season".

THURSDAY 10TH MARCH

A great start for England. Zat will cheer up Robbo. It is funny being injured. It has given me some time to paint again. I have done a surrealist portrait of Jimmy Hill. It came from ze depths of my subconscious. My son Raphael, who is only four, says it looks like a "Big arse botty". Great Balls Of Sacha Distel I shouted with delight. Zat is what I was aiming for.

FRIDAY 11TH MARCH

My brother Joel arrived at ze house sobbing his eyes out. He'd been told he was too crap for Peterborough - "Zere is only one place for you to go to now" I told him...."Here's Sergeant Wilko's phone number".It is time to go trophy hunting.

SATURDAY 12TH MARCH

Peter Streudal went off his trolley today against Charlton...but it is not fair on ze rest of us for him to get sent off. He must learn zat zere is such a thing as responsibility!

WEDNESDAY 16TH MARCH

Giggsy showed us another of his love letters from ze young girl fans. Zis one was from a nice Jewish girl called Hemlah inviting him round for Motzah balls. "What do they do with the rest of the poor Motzah" said Sparky. United were as hot as Dijon mustard tonight. I scored a couple of petite crackers as we stuffed Sheffield Tuesday 5-0.

SATURDAY 19TH MARCH

Sacre Bleu! I avv add a run-in with another little man by ze name of Hill...is zere some clan of zese half-witted Hill's somewhere. Ze press were all up in arms because I had pressed my studs into ze belly of some little man who was buzzing round my legs. Zat was a storm in a tea-cup. Ze whole day was crap. Who says irony is dead when zere in-bred supporters can chant: "It's Swindon Town, Swindon Town FC, we're by far the greatest team the world has ever seen". Not exactly mes amies. Anyway, zey will soon fuck off back to ze Endsleigh where zey belong. And what's more, zat Brian Killtime is so ugly, with a stupid little pony tail. He looks like ze south end of a north bound

camel.

SUNDAY 20TH MARCH

Ze farty little press pack are all Eric-bashing. It is pretty galling to be lectured at by people who are considerably more stupid zan oneself. So zey are slagging me off. I fart on zese people. And was it ever thus. Ze great philosopher Voltaire wrote in 1767: "Ze infamous trade of vilifying one's colleagues to earn a little money should be left to cheap journalists".

MONDAY 21ST MARCH

I am going to get a lengthy ban. Ze players have all been great and are trying to keep my spirits up - even ze Bogman came up and told me a joke: "What's the definition of a Yorkshire girl who is still a virgin? - one who can run faster than her brother".

TUESDAY 22ND MARCH

A strange, long day. Monsieur Eric is in ze doghouse again. Zere was lots of good banter on ze way down. Lee Disco Sharpe was going to be back in ze team and was all high about it. Ze lads were joking zat zey are so biased against United at ze BBC zat Alan Hansen would say it was unfair if Lee scored because ze Arsenal defence would be unfairly confused by it saying Sharp on ze back and front of Lee's shirts and zey would not know which way he was running. On ze coach Bogman had bad wind and it was smelling out ze whole vehicle. Zere is something too potent about ze gas on Leatherette seats. "Urrgh, I can smell it from here", shouted Fergie at ze front. Bogman has been banned from eating any more dried fruit and lentil beans.
Ze Red card I got was annoying. Ze little prick in black just wanted ze publicity. He is about as straight as a butcher's hook. Even ze Arse-nil players said zat I was trying to get out of ze way of Donkey Man Adams...well who would want hoof prints all down zere legs? And hasn't he got big ears as well - he could pick up Sky TV with zose lugs.

FRIDAY 25TH MARCH

Zut alors. Ze Today paper avv tried to do a secret diary of ze Monsieur Cantona. It is absurd; it reads like someone copying out Pass Your French A Level With Flying Colours. Touche. Zat paper is going down ze pan if you ask me.

SUNDAY 27TH MARCH

Great Balls Of Sacha Distel! I am not a happy Monsieur Cantona. United were crap in ze Coca-Cola Final. Mad Les in goal tried to lift our spirits on ze journey back by telling us about ze trip a few of ze lads took to Harrods on Saturday. Apparently Clayton Blackhead saw a sign saying WET FLOOR - and he did! Zen he tried to impress some pretty little woman who was walking by, but she turned and snapped at him: "Are you as self-conscious as you should be". All ze lads fell about when Clayton came in wearing his new cowboy boots. He thinks it is all cool to be American and he keeps listening to some Texan country and Western singer called Randy Nickers. Robbo said zat we should all have a party to celebrate Clayton's second anniversary without a first team game. "Could we find a venue big enough to hold all the fans who'd want to come?" said Brucey Bonus. Ze lads had not laughed as much since zey first saw Roy Keane As Mustard's goaty Beatnik beard.

WEDNESDAY 30TH MARCH

Zis was my last game for a while and it was a little pissoir of a match. Ze main thing was zat we beat ze Scousers 1-0. Andrex Andrei nearly gave away a penalty and it brought on a vintage Fergie fury. "If you get in that situation again you fucking Cossack, I'll send you out to a Salt Mine!", he roared. Zat Ian Rush really is a human curiosity. If he was on hard drugs he could inhale Peru. Ze lads were amazed to see ze girlie-wirlie zat Steve Macspamamam brought to ze players bar - she had so much acne Incey joked zat if we had a felt tip pen we could all play connect ze dots on her face.

THURSDAY 31ST MARCH

It is holiday time for Eric for three weeks. I avv decided zat I need solitude, so I will go to Euro Disney as no-one else seems to go there.

SUNDAY 3RD APRIL

Ze Blackbum players are all crowing because zey beat United. He who laughs ze last laughs ze weirdest - or so my senile old aunt Francesca de Peppercorn Cantona told me today. She fed me some onion soup and said: "Zat will get rid of some of your aggression Eric".

MONDAY 4TH APRIL

Dion Belfast was ze United hero against Oldham Athletic (now zere is a contradiction in terms). He came on as a substitute to score. Ze

Our Eric explains to a certain guitar player the ephemeral nature of Idolatry

French teletext Grand Oracle must have been trying to be funny - it said zat ze United defence was so slow again, it looked like Bet Lynch must have been playing.

SATURDAY 9TH APRIL
A panicky call from ze PFA, could I returnez for ze PFA Awards as I was ze Players' Player of the Year. Can zis be ze same Monsieur Eric zat everyone is supposed to hate?

SUNDAY 10TH APRIL
Kiddo said zat today's display against Oldham was ze worst of ze season - zat is right up until Sparky scored his fabulous goal. Gordon McQueen was on ze radio about ze game, but only Robbo could remember him and I must have misheard him because he said he was a big defender with "child-bearing lips". Ze PFA ceremony was good fun. It is a stonking great trophy. I add to show zat I can speak a little English, but I still managed to do my funny accent. I said zat I thank all ze people, even zose who did not vote for me - and I was looking at Alan Shear Envy when I said zat.

WEDNESDAY 13TH APRIL
I took my little frere Joel Cantona to ze Maine Road and ze lads put on a hell of a display. Robbo - and without his corset, amazingly - was how ze tabloids say a warhorse and Andrex Andrei scored a wonder goal. United are through to ze FA Cup Final. "I wonder who will present ze Cup" said Sharpey. Ze other lads will have to watch him if it is Her Majesty. Ze only time Sharpey has seen the Queen is on a stamp and he might feel inclined to lick ze back of her head.

THURSDAY 14TH APRIL
I avv given an interview in L'Equipe about zat little turd in black, Callow by name Callow by nature. I said he is a small boy who always wets his pants or something like zat. Funnily enough, zey did not leave in ze part where I called him Mister Ugly Bollock-Chops!

FRIDAY 15TH APRIL
Back training with ze lads. Fergie was so pleased with Bogman's volleyed goal against Oldham zat he bought him a present. "What is it gaffer?" said Gary Pally (it is true, we all speak like ze tabloids say). Fergie said: "It's a guide to Proctology". "What the fuck is that" said Paul Nosey Parker, being true to his name. "Look it up" said ze Boss. Brucey Bonus hurried and found a dictionary and read out:

"Proctology: the branch of medicine concerned with the anus and rectum". Everyone laughed and we were all expecting Bogman Denis to be excited when he was handed the book, but all he said was: "Has it got colour illustrations?"

SATURDAY 16TH APRIL

Zere was a mighty cheer around ze dressing room at 4.47 when We Won't Bottle It Blackbum lost at Ze Dell. United should have taken advantage but we lost on a slagheap pitch to a slagheap team. Fergie was so anxious he must avv got through seven packets of Orbit chewing gum. It was not helped zat one of our chief forwards, Brian McClard played ze whole game. He has got so tubby now zat ze club has had to buy him elasticated shorts. He's got more chins zan a Chinese telephone directory. When we all went to ze hard Rock Cafe and ze waiter said: "What do you want on your burger sir?", he said: "A hot dog!". He is ze only man at ze club who stands in front of a microwave shouting: "Faster!". When he had a headache once he could not take ze aspirin without a drop of double cream on it. When mosquitoes see Choccy they all shout: "Buffet"...Enough of zis tomfoolery.

THURSDAY 21ST APRIL

Bogman came into ze dressing room sobbing his eyes out saying zat Prince Charles had lost his little doggie and he was called Pooh. "So are you when you do those farts", said Sparky.

FRIDAY 22ND APRIL

Mad Dog Phelan has been saying zat he wants to bite me - I think I add better ask Jimmy McGregorian Chants for a rabies inoculation. Never mind what zat little dog turd was saying, his ugly face is grounds enough for ze PFA to charge him with bringing ze game into disrepute.

SATURDAY 23RD APRIL

Beat ze Bitter Blues 2-0. Zut alors! Steve the Macca is even fatter zan McClard. Ze referee booked Macca in ze fifth minute for elbowing me. I winced and ze ref asked me if I was alright: "It is not zat...it is his bad breath". Ze City players really put me off ze game. So much so zat I only managed to score twice within five minutes. Ze title charge is back on and Fergie had a smile as big as a Cheshire cat.

SUNDAY 24TH APRIL

Left a message on Alan Shear Envy's answerphone: "I don't think you were at ze Ready, Alan!".

WEDNESDAY 27TH APRIL

Back to ze home of ze Scum of England. Zey booed every time I add the ball, but in truth zey should avv been booing zere own team who were useless. Gordon Stricken was huffing and puffing so much on ze pitch zat I thought he was having an asthma attack. Zis result must really have got up ze nose of Sergeant Wilko because after ze game he was saying: "History will prove me right. I was reet to sell Eric". Funnily enough, Fergie just looked at me and winked.

FRIDAY 29TH APRIL

Zere was a big piss up after ze training session in honour of Dion Belfast scoring ze goal zat won ze reserves the Pontins League title on Wednesday night. Zen Fergie let slip zat part of ze United deal with Cambridge was zat zey would get an extra £500,000 when Dion played his first game for England. Brian Karate Kidd wet himself after saying zat zis was the funniest thing he had heard in ages. I did not think it was as funny as ze excuse McLard gave for stacking on ze stomach fat. "I put on a stone, but it was only eating fruit". "How is this so?" said Brucey Bonus. "I swallowed a whole plum and went up by a stone!".

SUNDAY 1ST MAY

Ze grass was so long on ze crappy Portman Road pitch zat I thought zey must be growing beetroot on it. Peter Streudal could not catch a cold at ze moment. Ze title race is all but over. Let Alan Shear Envy win ze Football Writers' Award. I will just have to buy a bigger display cabinet for all my League Championship medals. I did not avv ze best of games but on ze coach home we all agreed on ze highlight of ze game.
"Was it my goal dudes?" said Giggsy (he only really talks like zat to ze obese urine-smelly men who call themselves football reporters).
"Non!!!" was what we all cried.
It was ze headbutt zat Bogman did on zat Permy-haired wanker who looked like a clone of Terry McDimwit.

WEDNESDAY 4TH MAY

All ze players have been going on about zis Le Pissier. We all sang a song in his honour - "Big nose, he's got a fucking big nose, he's got a fucking big nose" to the melody of blue moon...Ah, ze dressing room wit!

ZE FINALE - CHAMPIONS AGAIN

I am a Champion again. Ze league is in ze bag. And now, as they have in Australia, we're off to do some drawf hurling at Wembley. I avv a new statistic for ze papers...it has now been three years since United have not won the league! I am a very, very happy Monsieur Cantona.

SATURDAY 14TH MAY

We avv won ze deuble! I love zis Wembley pitch. I should avv ad a hat-trick, but never mind as I also won ze money from zat midget Dennis UnWise. I was about to take ze first penalty when he came up speaking zat stupid cockerney eels and cockels pie talk and said: "Ere mate, I bet ya hundred nicker you miss!".

"I am not interested in knickers, you little dwarf, but I will take your money even zough you obviously need it for a better class of hairdresser." Ze celebrations zat evening were superb. At four in ze morning, a red-faced Govanite was dancing on the table singing: "Shit on the Kenny, shit on ze Kenny today", and I don't think he meant Kenny Rogers.

SUNDAY 15TH MAY

A brilliant procession, but zere was a fat little lady called Pauline hanging around Kiddo. Funnily enough, she smelt of wee too.

TUESDAY 24TH MAY

I am on tour with France in Japan and I am 28 years old today. I think zat is half Robbo's age. He has gone to Middlesbrough and taken Clayton Blackhead with him. I share a birthday with Bob Dylan, so I started singing Hey Mr Tangerine Man, but Jean Pierre Papin, who was a bit of a hippy in his younger days, swore at me for some reason.

THURSDAY 26TH MAY

I scored a header as we beat Japan. Zis was not hard as my marker was only four foot one tall. It is a funny old world, because he said zat all us Europeans look ze same. I was going to eat some raw fish after ze game, but I remember zat Gary Liveouthere did zat and got worms. Ze funny things was zat zey all looked like Donkey Adams.

SUNDAY 19TH JUNE

Yesterday I saw Ireland beat Italy 1-0. I am in ze land of ze free and home of ze brave to commentate on ze World Cup Finals. Unfortunately, I add to sit near zat John Mottyson. He's is ze biggest bore in ze continent. He is what ze lads call an Anorak, but he gave me Anoraknaphobia. He even started to tell me about ze Highway routes he add taken to get to ze ground. "I am sorry," I said, "but your are ze most dismal fart I avv met since a certain Swiss referee and I refuse to listen to your verbal diarrhoea". After zat I paid a visit to see Denis Bogman at ze Irish camp. He looked exhausted but I thought it only polite to ask him about his bowels. "How are your movements, Bogman?" He looked very unhappy and said: 'Ahh, Monsieur Cantona,' (he's always such a polite little Bogman) 'I am crapping as regular as possible. You could set your watch by it - 7am every day I have a crap.' "But what on earth is ze matter with zat?" I said. 'Well I don't get up until eight!'

MONDAY 20TH JUNE

I avv tipped Ireland to win ze World Cup - not zat I believe a word of zat merde. I could not believe Andy Townsend's hairstyle. I think he must avv been modelling his hair on Sharon Stone. Roy Keane As Mustard was telling me zat he is very vain about his hair and sits under a hairdryer wiv a big net every evening. Sadly I did not get away before Keano told me a joke. 'Where do French gun freaks go to enjoy themselves...the Rifle Tower." I think ze must avv shaved of some of his brains when ze gave him zat stupid marine's hairchop.

SATURDAY 25TH JUNE

I avv add to sit through Saudi Arabia v Morocco. It was so dull even Motty would avv been a relief. I avv been told zat United have sold Mike Phelan-leftout to ze West Bromy Albions. Poor old Mike. Ze only fan mail he got last season was a letter from a fat lesbian asking to borrow £50. He spent all last season in ze reserves. I thought of him when I was reading my Baudelaire, who said: "Life is a hospital in which each patient believes zat he will recover if he is moved to another bed."

WEDNESDAY 13TH JULY

I avv hit ze headlines. I was put in ze handcuffs after getting into a row before ze Brazil-Sweden semi-final. I avv never been in handcuffs before, but I understand zat it is quite a common experience for a certain Scouse player. It was all because of zis little turd of a security guard. Ze all behave in a fuckyou sort of way and I wasn't avving it! "Don't talk to me like zat you little arsehole", I said before landing him a blow on ze job. "What is more, you little fuckwit from ze land of humming electric chairs (I was in ze full Monsieur Cantona flow), you can take your stupid baseball and shove it where ze sun does not shine. Ze only reason zat it is your national game is zat it is so slow zat any idiot can follow it." Ze sweaty fat hacks were all running about trying to get a story, so I put my dark glasses on, turned my baseball cap round and sang Roy Orbison songs. Still my bust-up did not make as much of a storm as ze Chris 'Zat will be £20 extra if you chunder in my cab' Sutton affair. I am sure he is a candidate for Mensa. Not. Zat will really raise ze standards of Blackbum Rovers.

SUNDAY 17TH JULY
So Ze Brazilians avv won ze World Cup. I hate to make ze strange boasts, but I think Manchester United would have beaten either team.

WEDNESDAY 20TH JULY
Back to ze pre-season training. I think zat Steve Brucey Bonus as been wined and dined too much by ze Red Spews fanzine — he looks like he as put on two stone. Zere was even a new player called David May-notgetinzeteam. He was telling us about ze Blackbum team last season. Zat David Nora Batty certainly seemed to like ze showers. He was a true Yorkshireman. Ze all wear clogs, you know, because ze are too thick to do up shoelaces.

TUESDAY 26TH JULY
A glamorous pre-season friendly in Burnley. United won 3-2. We arr off to ze Ireland at ze end of ze week. Ze lads keep going on about ze Guinness zat you can drink. Apparently it turns your stools black. "So does eating coal," said Lee NotsoSharpe. He has learned a new dance for ze season. He calls it ze wiggle-diggle dance. It originated in Zambia where it involves two transvestites and a tube of Colgate. I hope zat lad is going to behave himself next season.

SATURDAY 30TH JULY
We arr in Dundalk. Incey thought zat it was where ze D-Day landings were!

MONDAY 1ST AUGUST
We beat Shelbourne 3-0. I scored a penalty to make amends for ze

miss on Saturday. Ze highlight of ze game was Giggsy being kissed, when taking a corner, by one of ze Nolan Sisters - Paul Nosey Parker was jealous because the only person on the trip who offered to kiss him was John Sadarse.

FRIDAY 5TH AUGUST

We got ze bus up to Glasgow. Brucey Bonus was cracking jokes - "What do you you call Yorkshiremen who have an IQ of 180?'" - "a City!". Zen Sparky chirped up - "What do you call a pretty girl in Glasgow?" - "a tourist!". Crap match. Zese friendlies are about as interesting as Graham Failure's team talks.

SATURDAY 6TH AUGUST

Zut alors! Now I know what zey mean when they talk about Pavlov's Dogs - zese Rangers fans have all ze charm of a night out with Mad Dog Phelan...and almost as much spit. I was sent off again, another Hitler in black - do they comb the local mental hospitals to find zese people. I av one answer for everyone - "Shit, Shit, Shit, Shit, Shit, Shit, Shit" I shouted in ze dressing room. Unfortunately, Bogman fainted with joy.

SUNDAY 14TH AUGUST

Ze new season is here. I saw a pale Alan Shear Envy at the players bar at Wembley. "Would you like a prawn sandwich" I said, and then "here's to another season of giving Blackbum the shits!" Ze wait is over...We hope to avv more trophies zan a demented game hunter! It feels great to be in ze Red shirt again!

MONDAY 22ND AUGUST

I am still banned because of ze Rangers incident, so while ze lads were playing at Notts Forest, I went out for a Chinese meal with my wife. "Please use ze chop sticks" said ze waiter. "But I only want ze chicken and sweetcorn soup". I saw some of ze game on TV. Stan Cauliflower gave ze defence problems...it seems he does so in and out of court! I don't like zere manager, he has a strange hair lip, like our old donkey Pierre in ze vineyard in Alsace-Lorraine.

SATURDAY 27TH AUGUST

Jimmy McGregorian Chants successor as physio, David-Saturday-Night-Fever, got his first taste of ze coach journey to games for our match at Tottenham. He started to tell us how much better our facilities were compared to Wigan's and shouted out: "look...the toilet even has soap". Bogman got all excited at zis and began telling Fever all ze different expressions for going to ze toilet zat he has picked up on his worldly travels. I am sure zat Bogman was foaming at ze mouth as he rasped: "In Canada they say 'I'm going to lay a log' and in Cuba they tell people they're 'heaving a havana', in Russia they 'fire the brown torpedo' and in China they...". 'Enough of zis crap' shouted Fever as he threw his sponge at him. "Exactly", shouted Bogman as he went to 'pump ship'. He's so obsessed, he even enjoyed ze toilets in Latvia! We left a very sour Kraut at White Hart Lane as we won 1-0 with a Brucey Bonus header.

WEDNESDAY 31ST AUGUST
Back in ze team for ze visit of Wimbledon. Vinnie Groans was wandering around mumbling and cursing like one of zose unfortunates zey keep in zat home in Longsight. I did not rate zat Reg Holdsworth player ze Dons have, but it is nice zat zey let someone with learning difficulties be zere manager. One day, hopefully, he will be able to get through ze whole sentence without a swear word. We won ze game easily.

THURSDAY 1ST SEPTEMBER
My son Raphael is getting to be a cheeky little rascal. We bought him a top from Baby Gap and he was going round with his collar up. Even at ze age of five he is funnier zan Pally. "Eric, mon pere" he said. "Where would you find a turtle without any legs?". 'I don't know', I replied. "Where you left him!". He has brought me a little toy to play with in ze big bath after ze games. I will have to watch it, zough, because Sparky sunk my last one.

FRIDAY 2ND SEPTEMBER
Fergie was looking at me in ze briefing room before ze tactics discussion. He drew a picture of a ball on ze blackboard and a goal. Zen he pointed to ze ball and said: "This is a ball. You kick it. You kick it towards the goal". "Monsieur Ferguson" I said, "I can understand English well enough". 'I'm not talking to you, Eric, I'm trying to explain what's going on to David Maynotbeinzeteamforlong'. Ze lads were all talking about zis David Maynotbeinzeteamforlong in ze pub afterwards. "Don't be unfair, he lacks only one things" said Incey. "What's that" asked Brucey..."Ability" we all roared.

SATURDAY 10TH SEPTEMBER
Tomorrow we go to ze Yorkieland. Zere have been many reports

about how un-welcome ze Yorkies made me when I was living zere and how ze hate campaign forced me out of ze area and to move to ze Salford. Ze truth is zat I was being driven mad by ze sound of zere clogs banging on ze streets all day and night. Zey arr stupid people, too. Zere was a woman in ze street who was always having babies. She had five kids and was expecting another. When I asked her why she was looking so worried, she said: "Well, I'm going to have another child".

"What is so wrong with that" I said.

"Well, I read in the paper yesterday that every sixth child in the world is Chinese".

Sacre Bleu!

SUNDAY 11TH SEPTEMBER

Ze Leeds fans were chanting as zough zey had won ze Cup Final. I think it was because zey had a crowd of over 10,000 at last. Fergie was not pleased with ze display and he would not share any of his chocolate-covered rich tea biscuits on ze journey home. He is also annoyed at all ze publicity zat Giggsy is getting again and he was shouting something about Ryan going out with Yogi Bear. Zis will please Raphael, as he likes zat character very much.

WEDNESDAY 14TH SEPTEMBER

Ze lads did brilliantly to beat ze Gothenburg. Zese Swedish people are so friendly, but if zey have a goalkeeper like zat it is no wonder zat so many commit suicide. Zere was lots of reading going on in ze players bar before ze game. Roy Keane As Mustard was looking at 'Lady Chatterley's Lover' and saying things like: "You don't see malarky like that in Cork". Paul Nosey Parker was reading a pocket guide to Psychology zat was called 'How To Cope With Rejection.' I think it was left here by Mike Phelanleftout. Incey was magnificent against ze Swedes. You can tell when he is really determined because his eyes get all big and bulgy and he starts to look like ze man in zat new film called Mask.

FRIDAY 16TH SEPTEMBER

I went to ze cinema zis afternoon to see Clear and Present Danger. It sounds like ze right title for ze story of a trip to Istanbul. I only went to see ze Reebok advert zat I avv made. Ze kept in ze bit where I say "Shit". Zis silly old woman behind me said: "Who the bloody hell is that, Gerard Depardieu?" How can ze compare me with him. He is ze sort of uncouth man who drinks straight out of ze bottle.

SATURDAY 17TH SEPTEMBER

Zose Scousers are something else...ze even stole ze salt and pepper pot from ze players dining room. It was a strange old game. Ze had Jan Mouldy in midfield who was so fat zat I was worried he was going to explode at one point. Zat Neil Fattock is an idiot. He kept niggling and elbowing me throughout ze game. "Shithead!" I said, to get his attention. "You have a kind face." He smiled so I added quickly: "Ze wrong fucking kind!" Zen I stamped on his legs and zen one of zose sad little petty bureaucrats showed me another of zose pretty little yellow cards. It was worth it. Brian Mclard scored a great goal and ze boss was all happy because we add beaten Liverpool. I think Kiddo has picked up on our worries about a certain defender. "I wouldn't want the job of cleaning David Maynotgetinzeteam underpants after that game," he said. I was wondering if zere was a clause in footballers contracts like ze ones you get from Allah Carpets — your money back if not totally satisfied! Even ze old Alan Hansen was having a go at May on Match of ze Day. My wife felt a bit sorry for him but said with a mischievous grin: "In his defence, he is playing well out of position ... on a football field."

SUNDAY 18TH SEPTEMBER

Ze Blackbum players at Chelseasick were all playing with zere collars up. Zat is ze nearest to genius zat they will get.

MONDAY 19TH SEPTEMBER

John Fash ze Bash has been having a go at me in ze tabloids papers. I am sure zat Gary Mabbutt could fill zem in far better on what makes a dirty player.

WEDNESDAY 21ST SEPTEMBER

Fergie played our Primary School IX against Port Vale and ze won 2-1. All ze stupid arseholes ringing in to complain zat ze weren't going to see me and Giggsy play. Do zey actually believe zat we want to go to zere poxy little ground - especially when ze Coronation Chicken Street iz on ze box. I am enjoying ze Street at ze moment but I wonder how Vinnie Samways finds ze time to play Deidrie's new Moroccan lover Shammy Leather.

FRIDAY 23RD SEPTEMBER

Zat Pauline smells of pee woman was hanging around outside ze Cliff again. She was telling anybody zat would listen, "I am Kiddo's friend. His best friend. Really. You've got to believe me. He wrote me

a letter once." She is so ugly and dwarflike. Zis started a conversation about small women. Pally had a copy of ze new Sky magazine and was talking about ze nudey picture of Kylie Minnyogre. He said zat he really likes petite women. But Denis Bogman said zat when he was a boy he was really turned on by ze thought of Hattie Jaques in crotchless underwear. I think I prefer it when he talks about irritable bowel syndrome.

SATURDAY 24TH SEPTEMBER

Ze game at Ipswich was strange. Nobody noticed until half-time that David Maynotgetinzeteam wasn't playing. Ze noise of farmers crunching pieces of straw between zere teeth was really quite off-putting. After ze game, which we lost 3-2, Lee NotsoSharpe was going round saying: "No worries, Dudes." Zat boy is an idiot. He has taken up a new fashion of wearing tank tops because he says zat is ze new craze in clubland.

MONDAY 26TH SEPTEMBER

Ze lads were all talking about ze Galacrapparay trip. I hated it zere last year. I spent ze entire time in ze hotel playing chess with Peter Streudal. He plays like he goalkeeps — rushing out of defence all ze time. I did not like ze Turks much and I said to Giggsy: "Whatever you do, avoid a Turkish bath." I only say zis because it must be ze only bath in ze world zat leaves you smelling of goat shit. Ze all had zis funny aroma around zem — even ze women. I think I shall send a donation to ze Kurds!

TUESDAY 27TH SEPTEMBER

I went to ze cinema again to see Roy Keano Reeves in Speed. Now I think I know where Giggsy got ze idea for his new haircut. Reebok were not happy with ze new hair crop but Lee NotsoSharoe said: "Cool dude, it's a winging fuzz cut". Zese boys get hyper active from drinking zere diet pop. Ze boys have all left for Turkey - so I watched Trelleborgs beat ze Blackbum. "You'll never win in Europe" I sang after ze game. I bet now zat Kenny Dogleash will be asking for more millions, zere is a French phrase which means roughly "To pick up a penny from the shit with your teeth". It was a figure of speech for zose who all stop at nothing to find gold. Somehow I always think zat it applies to ze Rovers.

WEDNESDAY 28TH SEPTEMBER

United got a good point against ze scummy Gallacrapparay. Zere was all zat talk about ze fearful Turkish fans but all zey did was whistle all game. Whistle out of zere arses more like. Wait till ze come to Old Trafford...zen ze will find out what an atmosphere is all about.

SATURDAY 1ST OCTOBER

A game against Everton. We were missing Giggsy, who has strained his calf muscle trying to crap over a hole in ze ground zat passes for a toilet in Turkey. Ze boy was lucky as ze game against Everton was, ow shall I put it, fucking boring! It was so dull zat I felt myself liquefying like an old Camembert. After ze game Mike Walkover was stumbling around saying: 'can anyone tell me who I've just signed'. He had ze look of a condemned man.

SUNDAY 2ND OCTOBER

Ze lads were all reading ze News Of The Screws, which was all about ze Princess-Dying-For-It and her Major-Has-It. Zis was nothing to ze scandal zat I ad just been told. Zat Tory MP Milligan who died of suffocation. Well everyone knows zat he was found trossed up in women's clothing and black binliners. But ze police also found him wearing a Manchester City scarf but ze hushed it up to spare his family ze embarrassment.

MONDAY 3RD OCTOBER

Training was dull today. I think zat Andrex Andrei is getting a bit big for himself with his jokes. "Did you know zat Franny Lee's toilet paper factory was robbed...but the police have nothing to go on". It was only Paul Nosey parker who laughed - but zen again he thinks Hale and Pace are funny.

TUESDAY 4TH OCTOBER

Listen to ze radio Five. Leeds get knocked out by Mansfield. I think I will send Sergeant Wilko a packet of Out-Of-The-Cup cakes!

FRIDAY 7TH OCTOBER

Sheffield Tuesday tomorrow. I am not going but all ze lads are hoping to get zere early enough to see Trevor Francis's car being attacked...

MONDAY 10TH OCTOBER

Ze lads were telling me about Sheffield Tuesday. Brucey Bonus thought he must be seeing things when Frank Skinner came out for zem...but Pally told him it was Andy Sinton and zey just look alike.

SATURDAY 15TH OCTOBER

Beat Wets Ham 1-0. Scored ze easiest goal in all my time at Old Trafford. Alvin Stardust froze in ze box and Giggsy gave me it to tap in.

MONDAY 17TH OCTOBER

My wife Isabelle was telling me zat she had been to a Physics lecture at Leeds University this afternoon. Ze old man giving ze talk, Bobby Stokes, ze uncle of Doris, said to ze audience: "How many people have seen a ghost?" About 100 of ze 200 people zere put up zere hands. "And how many of you have touched a ghost?". Zen about 50 people put up zere hands."And how many of you have had sex with a ghost?" Zere was a big laugh but zen one old Yorkshireman at ze back put his hand up. "I only ever ask that question for a laugh" said the lecturer - "no-one has ever put their hands up. Come on down"

"Sir, tell us" he said to ze old man, "about having sex with a ghost".

"Ooh, I'm reet sorry", said the old Yorkshireman, "I thought you said goat".

SATURDAY 22ND OCTOBER

Zat old Manchester Shitty were on Match Of Ze Day beating Tottenham. Ze were talking a load of Eartha Kitt about it being a great match. Zat Des Lemon and Trevor Boring had obviously seen a different game. Ze were going on about Jurgen Klinnsmann, but as Sparky said, ze never tell you what his father did during ze war, do zey?

SUNDAY 23RD OCTOBER

Beat Kenny Dogleash's side 4-2. Ze had Henning Berk sent off for a vicious tackle on Lee NotsoSharpe. Ze must have about five genuine home fans at ze Ewood Park. All ze talk was of Roy Keane As Mustard telling a girl zat she should go back to her council flat while he lived in a £500,000 mansion. "But you grow potatoes in the dining room, Roy, who'd want to go to your place?", said Incey. Roy looked all crestfallen. He has been very touchy ever since we have all been taking ze piss out of his silly beard. "What have Roy and Nicky got in common?" said Paul Nosey Parker. "Well they've both got the face of a Butt". No-one laughed zat much because Paul isn't zat funny. He thinks he is a wit. He's half right.

SATURDAY 29TH OCTOBER

Terry McDimwit opened our dressing room door by mistake and we all shouted out: "Calm down, calm down". He scuttled away and so did Newcastle on ze pitch.We gave zere team a lesson this afternoon. Ze may have just beaten our Primary School XI on Wednesday in ze Lemonade Cup but today ze met ze real stuff and ze could not cope. Our Dammon Hill-look-a-like Keith Gullible scored a cracker of a goal to seal ze win. Kevin Peegun, who'd borrowed Vera Duckworth's hair for ze day, was moping around afterwards. Ze only blot on ze day was zat none of our children were zere to see it. It would have been child cruelty to risk exposing zem to Peter Beardo's face.

SUNDAY 30TH OCTOBER

Everyone was reading about Giggsy's love life in ze Sunday papers. "Why is it that no-one ever talks about me?" said David Maynotgetinzeteam. "Because you're about as interesting as an episode of Brookside" said Pally.

MONDAY 31ST OCTOBER

It is funny flying out with ze rest of ze players. Ryan and Nicky spent ze trip larking about throwing bits of paper at Kiddo's head. "We're going into EEC territory now, Kiddo" said Fergie. "There's a directive banning self urination". Ze lads all laughed. All except Paul Schoolboys come to think of it. Zat may have been becasue he had to sit next to him on ze plane. Zere was going to be a lottery over ze seats but zen Incey said zat anyone with carrot hair didn't have a say. Gary Walshrabbit was looking all worried, but I noticed zat when Peter Streudal was asleep Walshy put his seat into tilt mode saying: "That'll do his back in". What can zis mean?" Arrived at ze hotel in Barcelona. Ze lads were all grounded so to cheer zem up I told zem zat me and Choccy would toast zem with San Miguel. Everywhere we went in Barcelona zat night zere were drunken Reds.

TUESDAY 1ST NOVEMBER

Peter Streudal got ze two bob bits after eating some Spanish omeletter. Ze only sympathy came from Denis Bogman Irwin who offered to sit by him on ze loo if he needed company. Terry Vegetables was in ze bar with Fergie. Ze were talking about some Panorama programme. For some reason he got all shirty when Fergie asked him if he took sugar in his tea.

WEDNESDAY 2ND NOVEMBER

United were ze biggest bucket of merde I have seen in my time zere. Zat Romario made Pally look like a great big lump of sick but I did not like him. He has zat spivvy Maradona look. On ze night United's best player was Dion Belfast. Afterwards everyone was really shell-shocked. Ze only one smiling was Bogman who said he managed to steal a bar of soap with Barcelona, Nou Camp written on it. But Fergie confiscated it saying zat BO now stood for Barcelona Ordeal. It was a frustrating game to watch. We were so bad zat the Spaniards next to me thought zat zey were playing ze other team from Manchester.

SATURDAY 5TH NOVEMBER

Manchester Shitty drew 3-3 with Southampton. Zat evening my little son Raphael asked if we could watch 'Bruce'll fix it'. It is Jim'll fix it I told him but he just gave me a big grin.

SUNDAY 6TH NOVEMBER

We bounced back well to beat ze Aston Vanilla. Ze were pissoir poor. Ze jolly fat Ron manager had been replaced by ze grumpy fat man. Zere was zis funny old bloke calling himself Doug who was just making hacking sounds and moving his hands as though he was preparing to sharpen knives. What can zis mean?

MONDAY 7TH NOVEMBER

Ze whole talk at training was of ze Sun allegations about match-fixing by Bruce Grubbylaard. "Why would anyone pay him to let in goals when zere is Dave Beasant who does it for free" said Brucey Bonus. Ze were saying zat Brucey Bonus had let in ze goals in our 3-3 draw at Anfield. Bogman was beside himself with rage: "Shit, turds and brown mushy arse bombs" he raged. "No-one on this planet could have stopped my free kick". Everyone wanted to know who ze mystery link-man footballer is and who ze short man is. One thing is for sure. We can definitely rule out Pally.

TUESDAY 8TH NOVEMBER

"Zere is another fix scandal" said Andrex Andrei. "Someone has, for 18 years, filled Manchester City full of crap players and managers just to give ze rest of ze country a good laugh". Zat is ze funniest joke Andrei has cracked since arriving.

WEDNESDAY 9TH NOVEMBER

Zis has been an amazing two weeks. Mike Street Walker has been given ze axe and so has Fat Ron and Ossie Ardiles. When we all heard of Fat Ron's dismissal zere were jokes about how quickly Coca-Cola goes flat. Fergie has been in a strange mood since Barcelona - eyeing everyone up with ze look of a funeral director measuring for coffins. Sparky is very grumpy at ze moment because he cannot get a proper contract extension. After all he has done for ze club zey should give him ze three years he wants. All ze lads agree with me on zis - mainly because we are all scared shit of the idea of having to play against him.

THURSDAY 10TH NOVEMBER

Another glorious United night. Ze Manchester Shitty really are so bad it's unbelievable. Zey are ze Derek Wilton of Premiership football. I scored a delicious little goal and Andrex Andrei was so fast zat ze City defenders must have thought he was doing a special Cossack dance. After all, he showed zem a clean pair of heels all night. Zat Mad Dog Phelan really is a disagreeable little arse wipe. Zat may be why Incey nearly cut him in half. Funny but at ze end I could not hear a single City fan.

FRIDAY 11TH NOVEMBER

Ze boss came into the training ground all red and seemingly furious. "I've just watched the Sky TV re-run Incey and I saw you say to Summerbee 'You're shit". "Sorry boss", said Incey. "Och it's not that lad. You're supposed to say 'You're fucking shit!'". We were all in such a good mood zat we only made David Maynotgetinzeteam clean half the toilets zis time.

FRIDAY 18TH NOVEMBER

My wife and I were invited over for a dinner party at Chateau Kanchelskis. Ze Andrei Andrex home is full of Mills and Boons books. His wife is a great cook but I can only say zat he eats food like he plays ze game. Head down, jerky movements and a few crumbs coming my way only every so often.

SATURDAY 19TH NOVEMBER

Zut alors! I take it all back. Andrex Andrei is ze best crosser in ze game. He set me up for a beauty of a header against Dismal Palace. Peter Streudal went off after five minutes with a bad back. He has been putting too much strain on it recently bending down to pick up old cigarette stubs down the Sir Matt Busby Way. Kevin Pilchardtin came in goal. He is from Hitchin. I thought zat was something you did on ze motorway.

WEDNESDAY 23RD NOVEMBER

Great balls of Sacha Distel. We cocked it right up again. I think zere is a bit of a phobia about ze European Cup...we start to play like Manchester Shitty. Ze Swedish climate did not help. It was grey and gloomy all day. And no wonder ze all top themsleves if ze have to pay £4 a pint. It was a funny trip all round. Zere were so many kids on ze United first team trip zat I thought we were in ze middle of a Grange Hill episode. I couldn't tell if Fergie was angry or just shocked. He did keep saying: "Fucking, fucking, fuck it" but I stopped counting after 521 times. When I got home Raphael just said: "Mon Pere. Plonkers!".

FRIDAY 25TH NOVEMBER

Ze lads were all agog. Paul Mersondrugs has been selling his story to ze Daily Tittle Tattle saying he was a junkie. It is funny but ze other papers did not get a sniff of it. Zat boy must have ze dopiest wife in England if she did not know he was on drugs. Zat would get right up my nose! He may get off a little bit because ze football authorities really hate it if players take performance-enhancing drugs - and he couldn't be accused of zat. David Maynotgetinzeteam was asked to take a dope test. As we all suspected, he proved to be one.

SATURDAY 26TH NOVEMBER

Sparky was unfairly sent off after zat Steve Marrowhead rolled about like a turd in a bottle. It was a nasty spiteful little game. Steve Going Bould was all donkey kicks (no need to ask about ze other one) but at least Incey got stuck in to a fat bit of Danish bacon. And boy, did he sizzle. Ze biggest surprise was seeing ze Chairman Martin Deadwood shouting ze abuse at ze referee after. On ze coach home all ze lads broke into a chant of: "Feared by the ref, loved by ze board. Eddie Wards, Eddie Wards, Eddie Wards"It is coming to something when at ze end of a tempestuous week at United I am seen as a model of restraint! Gary Walshrabbit came rushing up to me as we left ze coach. "I can't wait to get home and tear my wife's knickers off" he said. "Why is zat?" I asked politely..."Because they are killing me".

THURSDAY 1ST DECEMBER

Ze lads pinned an advent calander on ze wall. We are all allowed to open a door...If we are good. Giggsy got to go first because he is now 21 and all grown up. He can even wipe his own bum now - even zough Bogman keeps offering. My great Uncle Pierre Claret Cantona was over. He is still wearing a beret. He has such rancid old goat's cheese breath zat I left him talking with David Maynotgetinzeteam for three hours.

SATURDAY 3RD DECEMBER

We stuffed ze little Canaries. Ze all looked a bit tired but Jeremy Gossamercondom said zat ze had all been out late ze past week helping with ze pea harvest at ze chairman's farm.

SUNDAY 4TH DECEMBER

Ze Christmas preparations in ze Cantona house are getting exciting. Back in France, we do not really celebrate in such a big way. In France Christmas Eve is ze big day. But Raphael wanted to go to Santas Grotto. I took him to a big department store. It was all a bit cheapo and nasty. Santa was a Chinaman with bad breath and ze only presents he was giving away were signed pictures of Danny Wallace. He said zat ze new United Superstore had 8000 left over. Ze man who ordered zem had no idea about football. Zen neither did little Danny. I wonder what ever happened to him?

TUESDAY 6TH DECEMBER

It is now a week and two years since I avv been at Old Trafford. I feel very settled in here. I even have my own salt and pepper pot in ze players lounge. I was reading ze tabloid newspapers in zere. All ze lads had told me zat Arsenil were ze nost boring team in England. I don't think zis can be right. Cocaine addicts, players becoming pimps, drink drivers, handlers of stolen goods, brawlers in Butlins . . . ze avv more zan enough material to make zere own TV soap: ArseEnders. Incey says zat Mickey Rourke could play Paul Mersondrugs.

WEDNESDAY 7TH DECEMBER

We finally showed just what a pile of steaming great Turkish turds zat Galacrapparay are. We played our Primary School IX and won 4-0. Ze were spitting at us ze whole time. I think zat ze stories of zem eating rancid old kebabs all ze time is true. Gary Neville was spat at and he ended up with two bits of cucumber, a piece of chilli and a fraction of pitta bread on his cheek. We could not believe ze big twat with ze handlebar moustache who came on as a sub. "Get back to a fucking Sinbad movie, you tosser!" said Simon DJ Gary Davies. Zat lad definitely has potential. Ze all went off to Cheerleaders nightclub to celebrate. Ze usual crowd of wannabeaplayer'swife women were zere.

THURSDAY 8TH DECEMBER
I was stopped in ze street and asked to sign a copy of my new video Eric Ze King. Ze woman asked me if it was true zat I had seen a head-shrinker. Madness is like vomit, I told her. It is ze passerby who is incon-venienced.

FRIDAY 9TH DECEMBER
Joined up with ze French team as we were flying out to play a European Championship game in Auberginegoneoff. It was funny being able to talk ze French language again with players but ze were all commenting on how I avv started to pick up ze Northern accent. Why do you keep saying: "Sorted" zey asked. Oh well, I add better finish for ze evening. I hope zat ze lads win at Queens Bend Over tomorrow. I am looking forward to getting back for ze club office party. Ze youngsters David Beckenhambypass, Nicky Headbutt and Paul Schoolboys have to put on a pantomime. Ze got some dark looks when zey asked Brucey Bonus and Pally to play ze two ends of a pantomine horse. "Well you're used to going in differ-ent directions," said Headbutt. Zat lad has balls as big as saddle-bags. I wish all ze Reds a happy third title winning New Year. I am sure, too, zat Paul Mersondrugs is not ze only one dreaming of a white Christmas.

FRIDAY 16TH DECEMBER
Ze lads were all talking about ze sacked managers of recent times. "Why doesn't Ossie Ardiles look out of the window in the morning?", asked Brucey Bonus. "Don't know" we all yelled back. "So he's got something to do in the afternoon!". Manchester Shitty have signed a bloke called Maurizio Gaurdyourcarnow. He is supposed to have really good form. Personally I was amazed zat Arsenil didn't go in for him. He could have got ze cars zen Tony ManDonkey could have crashed them.

SATURDAY 17TH DECEMBER
We lost to ze Nottingham Forest. Stan Cauliflower scored a great

goal. He has ze sort of accent not heard since ze days of Crossroads. Ze whole match had a sour taste, zough, because Stuart Pieceofhisbrainmissing made certain bad remarks to Incey. I liked Incey's reply, though: "Wrong fucking player Stuart, wrong fucking century". What do you expect of some greasy-haired tit whose best days were in non League football. "He'll pay the penalty" for zat said Fergie. But apparently penalties are a sore subject with him. Zen again if he holds zese sort of views perhaps zat explains why he missed against Germany in ze World Cup. Fergie stormed into ze Press Conference and told zem all about it. He was in one of his tempers. Ze sort where he eats bread and it comes out toasted.

SUNDAY 18TH DECEMBER
I rushed into buy ze News Of Ze Screws when I saw ze billboard: "Fergie Aids Test!". Luckily it was ze fat Royal reject one.

MONDAY 19TH DECEMBER
My son is starting to crack ze funny jokes. Raphael came up to me and said: "Mon Pere, do you know what a penis is?". I thought zat he was going to talk about Brian Horton but he said, "A penis is a bloke that plays the piano".

TUESDAY 20TH DECEMBER
Zere was another annoying article by zat Jimmy OvertheHill. Zis time zat fugitive from a chin gang was telling Mike Atherton how he should Captain ze England cricket team. Zat man is such a plonker...when he was born ze should have kept the stork and got rid of ze baby. To use my old Uncle Pierre's curse, I hope he pisses vinegar the whole night.

THURSDAY 22ND DECEMBER
Christmas fever is building up at ze club. We are going to buy Kiddo a season ticket to ze zoo - he'll be less conspicuous zere.

FRIDAY 23RD DECEMBER
David Maynotgetinzeteam came up and asked Pally if he wanted to go for a Christmas drink: "I'm not that lonely" said Pally. Still, Maynotgetinzeteam does serve one useful purpose, I suppose, as a terrible example. We now all call him banana because he's always getting skinned.

MONDAY 26TH DECEMBER

Beat Chelseasick. Choccy scored ze winner and we played well. Drinking a pint of Bitter in ze players bar after ze match I saw Glenn WonHoddall singing carols and combing Ken Bates's beard. It was nice to make a monkey of zere goalkeeper Dimitri Sardine again. And zat Frank Spencer is so dumb. He thought zat ze English channel was a new cable station.

SATURDAY 31ST DECEMBER

It was Brucey Bonus's 34th birthday but he did not want to be reminded of it. Sparky had bought a birthday cake made of white chocolate for Brucey Bonus but zat cheeky Nicky Butthead said: "Be careful if you put the right number of candles on his birthday cake - it'll be a fire hazard. We drew 2-2 with Southampton. I set up Pally with such an easy chance zat even zat big giraffe couldn't miss it. Zat Matthew Le Pissier did not have a great game. I may have put him off a bit when I went past and said: "Is zat your nose or are you eating a banana?"

1995

TUESDAY 3RD JANUARY

First game of ze new year and it was on Sky. Dion Belfast was back and enjoying a joke with ze lads. He really is nice, zough he was telling us what a sick nodding dog Phil Kneel is. The only thing he's ever achieved on his own is dandruff. We won easily 2-0. Ze team were so young I thought we'd all have to sing Kylie Minogue songs at half-time.

SATURDAY 7TH JANUARY

Incey made a sick joke about Larry Grayson. He told me zat this bloke was a camp performer who used to say: "Shut that door" all ze time. "You know what 'is last words were, mate?", Incey said..."Shut that lid".

SUNDAY 8TH JANUARY

Preparing for ze FA Cup game at Sheffield by reading all ze papers. Arsewipe's Ian Fight Fight Fight got himself in trouble for comments about ze Millwall fans. Ze were incensed zat hesaid they were all liberals who believed in freedom for all. Zey demand the right to hate anyone regardless of race and creed. I avv been asked to write another book. Zis time in ze Philosophy of Monsieur Cantona. I think I shall do a chapter on violent behaviour. Everton's Druncan Ferguson would make a good case. We think zat Fergie is up to something. He keeps nipping off to use ze telephone and whispering about a bag of coal. Perhaps it is zis freezing Yorkshire weather.

MONDAY 9TH JANUARY
We are through to ze next round of ze FA Cup after a great performance. Sparky scored a rare header before I finished off ze blunt blades with a little delicate chip. Zen I did my Marlon Brando impersonation at ze thick Yorkshiremen.Fergie was in one of his ultra happy moods afterwards. He kept looking at Sparky and winking. Zere was something else odd too. Keith Gullible was carrying round a big suitcase saying: "Fuck me, I have got to go to the land of Nod. It's full of macho men in t-shirts who are all as obese as Gazza". I don't think he was talking about ze Hacienda. Harry Bassett was his usual witty self after ze game. He only said "wankers" 49 times. On ze coach back to Manchester Fergie put on a song called "Working in a coal mine" and was adding up on his calculator. Martin Deadwood went as white as a sheet, zough.

TUESDAY 10TH JANUARY
Great balls of Sacha Distel...Fergie has pulled off a real shock. Ze first we knew of it was when a mini-cab arrived to take young Keith away. Zen Lee NotsoSharpe Electronics rushed in and said: "Guess who the Gaffer has bought for £7 miilion quid?"
"Le Pissier?, Stan Cauliflower?, Lesbian Ferdinand?".
"No. No. Andy Cole"
"Andy, Andy Cole, When he gets ze ball, He scores a goal" we all sang. Zat explains Martin Deadwoods' face, I thought. Zat idea must have occured to Choccy because he said: "Seven million. That'll ruin stingy Martin's day. He's so mean that when he found a box of corn plasters last year, he started wearing tight shoes". David Maynotgetinzeteam then said: "I wouldn't want to be the person to tell Sparky". "You can fucking shut up" said Incey, "Your last performance was up to your usual substandard. It would only take about £7 to replace you!".

WEDNESDAY 11TH JANUARY
Off on ze international duty with France. We beat ze Dutch 1-0. I can't stand zat David Ginandtonic. He thinks he's a real Don Juan

with women but even ze pretty Paris girls Don Juan to have anything to do with him.

FRIDAY 13TH JANUARY

Ze dreaded Friday 13th. Peter Streudal looks back to his old self. "Zat is because he has stopped trying to keep up with ze youngsters and boogie all night at ze slipped Discotheque", I joked. I met up with ze Andy Colenotdole and he seemed a shy young man. Fergie called us all together and presented him with a bottle of brasso. "You'll need this son at Manchester United. You are going to have a lot of medals to polish". "Tell us the truth, Andy" said Giggsy, "It must have been torture to have to spend so much time looking at the face of Beardo the weirdo". "Well, let's just say he's in the 256th Day of a 14-day beauty plan" joked Andy. We all laughed at zat one. Sparky was very gracious - he came up and wished Andy Colenotdole all ze best. Funnily enough zough, he only talked in Welsh.

SATURDAY 14TH JANUARY

Stan Cauliflower did fuck all to stop Blackbum today. Ze lads were all laughing about his moody expression when he was told zat United had brought a £7 million striker. Apparently he's now known as Forest Grump. At ze hotel today we had to listen to another row between Incey and Damien Keane. All ze kept saying was: "I'm the guvnor", "No, I'm the guvnor!". I could not understand it because for three quarters of an hour I thought they were saying: "Mind the oven door". Denis Bogman Irwin was in a jolly mood as his wife has got better. He had had all ze in-laws staying but he calls zem "the out-laws". He told me he had said to his aunt: "why do women have smaller feet than men...so they can stand nearer the sink". Zen she had hit him round ze head with a piece of Irish soda bread.

SUNDAY 15TH JANUARY

A cold and blowy day in ze Northeast. United's dressing room was like an episode of Casualty. Brucey Bonus had, in Incey's Cockerney eel slang, ze two bob bits, and Bogman was complaining about ze cheap toilet paper ze have at St James Park. Zen poor old Sparky got carried off after scoring a brave goal. I did a clever little dummy zen Sparky scored a great goal but Pauvlos Snivelwreck came up with his legs whirling like a dervish. Zis upset us all because Sparky is one of my favourite team-mates. Zen Nicky Butthead got an elbow in ze face and had double vision. "Christ, you don't want to see two David May's" said Pally. We ended up scraping a draw. Ze were all fired up and Keano had a running battle with some skinhead on ze pitch. "You big poof" he kept shouting. After ze game Fergie was interviewed by zat Prick Collins, who didn't ask much about Sparky's injury and zen said: "Well you've just brought his replacement anyway". Fergie kept his cool on ze screen but we knew he was furious because when he came in he opened a bottle of beer with his teeth.

MONDAY 16TH JANUARY
Zut alors! Ze news about Sparky is better zan we had expected. He is a brave old battler. We teased Fergie today and said he should buy Dumbarton's great new striker, Angus McCoatup.

THURSDAY 19TH JANUARY
Before we went out for training Bogman was telling me about a cousin who had come up with a scheme to make money. He'd gone into his bank manager and said: "I want a loan to start up a cheese making factory in Leicester. I think the cheese should be a different colour, something like Red Leicester". "Don't be silly" the bank manager said, "That already exists. Don't come back until you've got a better idea". A week later his cousin went back and said he'd thought of a better idea...to make cheese in a place called ze Cheddar Gorge. "Now, you've not thought this through" said the bank boss. "I'll only see you again if you have thought it out preperly". 10 days later Cousin Bogman went back: "I've cracked it. I'm going to move to Israel and set up a factory there. The labour's cheap, it's nice to live and I've got the perfect name".
"What is it?".
"Cheeses of Nazareth!"

FRIDAY 20TH JANUARY
A good training session with Andy Colenotdole. All ze plonkers in ze papers have been going on about how difficult it will be with United's style but Kiddo - who wet himself when he was told about ze transfer - said: "I hope this isn't too complicated, but the plan is for Eric to pass the ball and Andy to shoot it into ze net". Amazingly, it worked 62 times in a row. Zere were lots of people watching ze training but I don't think ze are any who are keen on David Maynotgetinzeteam. Every time he got ze ball the entire crowd was hissing him. All except one man. He was applauding the hissing.

SATURDAY 21ST JANUARY

Getting ready for ze big game against Blackbum. Alan Shearenvy will be playing but not Nora Batty who is still injured. Lots of games were off because of ze heavy rain. I watched Match Of Ze Day but switched off because I cannot stand zat Gary Limited. He is so bland he makes Derek Wilton look controversial. If there's a good idea in his head zen it's in solitary confinement. Incey's all on a high after getting through a reserve game and scoring. Him and Giggsy were re-enacting scenes from International Gladiators. I did not win ze National Lottery again. Ze only number I got right was 31 - zat is for ze number of times I have wanted to strangle Cilla Black. Zat Blind Date is crap. I know people always think I am reading my Emile Zola or Jean Genet or Flaubert but sometimes I try to get into ze minds of ze young players. I don't think I will bother again watching it again. Oh well. An early night. We have to win tomorrow.

SUNDAY 22ND JANUARY

We beat ze Blackbum. It was a draining game but we played zem off ze park. Giggsy was back to ze boy wonder form - although he made it a testing little header for me to score. Zey equalised late on but it was disallowed. Alan Shearenvy wrestled Keano to ze ground and pulled his hair. Well, zat's how we all saw it! After ze game Fergie just stood outside Kenny Dogleash's room shouting: "Ahh! Ahh! Cheese rolls. Cheese Rolls!". Andy Colenotdole showed he has nippy little feet - and Graeme Lesick moaned more throughout the game zan Ian Fight Fight Fight. We are back in ze race!

MONDAY 23RD JANUARY

When I returned home after ze training zere was a funny message on ze ansaphone: "Ha, you stale French croissant, it's Danny Wallace here. I told you I'd make it at United, and I've been proved right - they've put my name down as one of the hundred heroes on the new United kit, so shove that up your brie stick and eat it!". I was so shocked zat I rang Birmingham to remonstrate with ze little toad, but when I rang zey said that he'd had to go to the hospital because he'd pulled his hamstring after he'd tripped over Karen Brady's stilettos...ze plonker!

TUESDAY 24TH JANUARY

Zis is some sort of strangely quiet week. Nothing out of ze ordinary is happening.

What a shitbag of a day. We were not staying in ze usual Shellsuit Park Hotel in deepest Snobburbia but were stuck out in East Croydon. All ze people zere had ugly "Saaaaf London" accents and, oddly, ze all looked like bulldogs. Zere was a little altercation at ze game at Palace so I was late getting home. When I got out of ze car Isabelle was already standing in ze doorway.

"Eric! Eric! Eric! You great big trufle-head", she shouted. "What happened?"

I told her what a crappy night I'd had.

"Ze Shithurst Park was like a giant cow shed and ze pitch cut up like a greasy sponge cake. Ze beautiful game is not how I'd describe having Richard Coleslaw kicking your heels every two minutes and I'd had enough. Zen after getting ze red card I had to walk along zis gravel track in front of a load of cretins. Ze next thing I knew was some little man in a cheap leather jacket shouted out zat Flaubert could not write for toffee. I gave him a chance to apologise but he carried on. So I clipped him round ze ear. Ze next thing ze were throwing tea at me and ze did not even have ze decency to make it sugared."

"Arrete. Arrete" Isabelle shouted. "Don't give me zat shit Eric. It's all over ze telly. Raphael said you were doing your Bruce Lee impression and even Great Aunt Marie-Claire rang from Toulouse and said she had seen you doing a kung-fu kick. Ze French TV had interrupted ze Bordeaux Over-50's Bowles tournament. She said it was just like ze kick you did on little John Paul Apricots when he stole your crayons at Kindergarten. Come on, Eric, tell me what happened?".

"My baby", I said, "I just flipped. I was so annoyed with myself for getting sent off zen zis little moron in a cheap leather jacket came bounding down like a contestant on Come On Down. He was spitting and jabbering. He looked like ze sort of man who couldn't count up to 20 without taking his shoes off - so dumb zat a mind reader would only charge him half price. Zen I am afraid ze fires of fighting inspiration engulfed my spirit..."

"You mean you drop-kicked ze little turd and gave him a good smacking!" Isabelle said.

"Zen Incey was called racist names and a fat dustman rammed his cheek into Incey's hand. 'We'll take you all!' Incey was shouting and Bogman Irwin was threatening to tell one of his jokes to them. Ze worst thing happened later...It was not ze Jolly Copper who talked to me but it was David MayNOWgetinzeteam. He was glaring at me ze whole jorney. Ze one time he had done something well for United

The TABLOID Journalist returns HOME

Wake up Marie I gotta tell yer I just had to cover the worst example of wanton distruction & terrifying violence the world has seen in 50 years. I have stared into the Face of Evil & seen a deed so Foul it will live on forever in the annals of infamy. Long will the civillised peoples of the Earth remember this day. When dedicated decent guardians of the peoples morals stood up to Shout loud from the Roof tops that we would bravely trumpet the rights of Good & the perpetrators of Devilry would be Shown up. I was there I told my tale I...

FUCK OFF Harry you were at Selhurst Park NOT Bosnia

TZAN

it wouldn't even get a mention in ze papers."

Isabelle put her arms round me and said: "It's all right my Eric, nothing is too much to bear". She is a wonderful woman. Zen she made me laugh by saying: "Thank Dieu you didn't see Sportsnight. Gary Limited came in his pants he was so excited. He really is a man who would be enormously improved by laryngitis".

Zere was only one final punishment...she said zat I had to go out in public in zat rancid multi-coloured coat-cum-blanket zat Blind Papa Burgundy gave me for Christmas. Now ZAT is what I call public shame.

THURSDAY 28TH JANUARY

Called in to see Fergie. I felt terrible. I don't give a shit about ze sanctimonious journalists but I was sorry zat I let down Fergie. He was supportive, zough, and said he would fight my corner in ze board battle. Ze TV must have shown ze incident 8000 times. All ze papers had me on ze front page. I avv been called a thug, a menace, a loon and an animal. I watched Animal Hospital to see if I was on it but zere was only a man with a bear.

FRIDAY 29TH JANUARY

I avv been banned for ze rest of ze season and fined £20,000. Ze lads say ze will win it for me! Ze Daily Star had an interesting story about ze man I kick-arsed with. He has a funny idea of how to use a spanner. He thinks you use zem for robbery and violence. Zen Graham Smelly at ze Fuckup Association said he was happy with what United had done. His very presence holds you smell bound. A long day but I was pleased with Raphael. He had asked me if all ze ugly little men hanging around outside ze house were ze perverty men his teacher had warned him about. Ze are ze hacks, Raphael. Ze are so seedy ze tremble every time ze meet a canary. Later, on ze BBC Six O' Clock News he stuck his tongue out at zem. Now zat is my boy! "Like father like son" said Isabelle proudly. Zis has been some day! I now have a break. Living is mostly wasting time, anyway. At least I will be able to watch my box set of Fawlty Towers at last. Ze United fans have been magnifique, zough.To zem I say, like Arnold Schwarzenegger, "I will be back".

SATURDAY 30TH JANUARY

After a heart-to-heart over a packet of Cadbury's mini cream eggs, Fergie has agreed zat I should go away for a while with Isabella and Raphael. First, zough, I avv to go to Paris for a Bic commercial. Ze papers are chock full of anti-French drivel. Zese people don't fool anyone...pretending to get het up about whatever issue zere editor has dragged zem out of ze pub to write about. Ze lads beat Waxcars easily in ze Cup...I still fancy us for ze double double. Would I get back in ze team? Another of ze Neville brothers played - he must have flown all ze way from New Orleans.

TUESDAY 7TH FEBRUARY

Incey sent me a fax in Guadeloupe saying zat he had been to the South Norwood police station in Letsby Avenue. He said zat one of the coppers had a face like a Saint...a Saint Bernard. 'Daarn't worry, mate', said Incey, 'I've been tried and found wantin'. Zat was a clever pun for Incey, perhaps it is one of Denis Bogman's. I left - I had promised Raphael I would play beach tennis with him. I don't see why anyone should complain about me being on holiday - I thought zat was social services policy in England. I wore my snazzy stars and stripes swimming trunks again.

FRIDAY 10TH FEBRUARY

Ze press have arrived in Guadeloupe. All ze residents are shocked...even in hot weather zese Englishmen still wear socks inside zere sandals on ze beach. Ze biggest grins were on ze faces of ze bar owners. Zese hacks have got a junket to fly out and harrass me. Most of zem are too pissed to tie up zere own shoe laces. Most of zem are so desperate to get laid away from zere wives zat ze have been asking how much is charged for Ramond, ze hotel goat. I sent a postcard to Kenny Dogleash saying 'you're shit and you know you are'.

SATURDAY 11TH FEBRUARY

A rumpus on ze beach. I was having a lovely time with Isabella and Raphael - playing with ze official souvenir Ryan Giggs beach ball - when zis dirty old man started peering out at us from ze palm trees. Isabella spotted him first...standing zere with a big erect camera: "I feel sorry for little pervs like that - such a little mind all alone in a great big head". Ze next thing I knew he was trying to take pictures of my pregnant wife in her bikini. Zis was enough to give all of us morning sickness. 'Mummy' said Raphael: 'Zat ugly man is shooting pictures of your pregnant belly - and he looks like zat ugly crap actor out of the Bill!'. I marched up to him and told him zere were cinemas in Soho for men like him. He had a nasty squinty eye. Still he would not stop filming and I warned him to leave ze private property beach:

"You are ze sort of person who would make a perfect stranger. Now pissoir off". Zen he said he was Mr Lies-through-his-teeth of ze Independent Broadcasting Company.

"Daddy" shouted Raphael: "Give him the Cantona foot massage". So I sang ze old Mud classic: "Zat's neat, zat's neat, zat's neat, I really love your Cantona feet" and kicked him up ze arse doing a neat little two-step dance. Zen Isabella and Raphael started lobbing old bits of puff pastry at him and ze rest of his dirty mac brigade. He was stumbling round on ze floor when ze Gendarme arrived. An old woman, who luckily happened to be sporting a Man United bobble hat, told zem she had seen ze whole thing - and said he looked like ze man who had been hanging around the little girls toilets ze day before: 'He's a menace - and he looks like that crap actor out of the Bill' she said.

Ze Gerdarme handed me ze film he had been taking and all ze people on ze beach sang: "Vive La France" followed by: "We're on ze march with Fergie's army". I gave Raphael ze film and he used it to tape up ze broken arm on his Mark Hughesy action man doll. In ze bar zat evening ze manager of ze hotel said zat he was proud to have me as a guest and to please send my regards back to our cousin Jacques Lefevire. Isabella shuffled up to me and told me she was so glad she married a real man.

SUNDAY 12TH FEBRUARY

Fergie rang me early this morning and asked what had been going on. Isabella grabbed ze phone and told him all about it. He was very angry with zose sleazy press people. 'Some of zem are one notch above grave robbers' he said, and 'don't worry' he added, 'I will tell ze whole world zat ze wretch got off lightly'. He was happy because we had beaten Manchester Shitty again. Zat was such a foregone conclusion zat I hadn't even bothered to ask. Andy Colenotdole had scored again and Denis Bogman's piles have cooled down. All in all, a fun-packed day.

SUNDAY 19TH FEBRUARY

Ze end of a great holiday. Ze pregnancy is going well. Just think, little Cantona junior could be born in England and could end up playing for zem in the 2114 World Cup! - zat will probably be held in Jupiter. By zen, Lee NotsoSharpe might even have begun to grow up. We flew to Paris first to collect some chic maternity wear. We have tried some of ze Mothercare stuff but it is about as appealing as United's blue kit. Ze top executives of Nike were zere. Ze said zat all zis so-called bad publicity was having a real effect on zere sales - ze were higher zan ever. A Paris fashion designer was asking me whether all English fans wore scuffed black leather jackets. "Only after ze've messed with me" I said. I watched ze FA Cup goals on ze TV. Brucey Bonus rose so well for ze first header against ze scum zat I suspect Fergie must have given him an enema before ze game. It was lovely to see Sparky score. Zat would have been madness to get rid of him...even if he is Welsh. And didn't mad Sergeant Wilko look happy at ze end. Raphael and me sang: "3-1, without Cantona" before bedtime.

TUESDAY 21ST FEBRUARY

Down to Sarth Norwood police station with Maurice Having Kittens. He did all ze talking saying I was sorry for kicking zat ugly thug. But he said it was a spur of ze moment thing, zat I lost my temper after being insulted. Zat is not as bad, I would think, as taking a spanner along to a robbery. Ze police were polite ze whole time but ze could certainly learn a thing or two about coffee. Ze muck ze served us was fit only for ze Executive boxes on match days. Isabella had dressed me up all smart in a waistcoat and suit. On no account, she said, was I to take zis off and reveal my Bruce Lee T-shirt underneath. Ze worst thing about ze whole day was zat zey released my full name - Eric Pierre Daniel Cantona - to ze papers. Luckily ze did not say zat I was named Pierre after old Pierre 'The Spitoon' Flauberton, who could gob ze length of seventeen hogs. Fergie was a bit anxious and kept saying: "You will stay, won't you?" about 800 times.

FRIDAY 24TH FEBRUARY

Ze FA have banned me until ze end of September. Zat gives me nearly eight months to finish putting together my MFI wardrobe. Isabella was pleased in a way - I will have no excuses for not helping with ze nappy changes now. In some of ze photos ze next day I look quite grumpy. Ze truth is zat I was transfixed by Graham Smelly's hair...I am sure he goes to ze same people zat Reg Holdsworth does in Coronation Street. And zat David Davies - such original minded parents he must have had when it came to choosing names - is about as interesting as the talking clock. Some of zese freeloaders care nothing for ze beautiful game. Fergie was livid on ze way home - but I said: "Don't worry about ze extra games, I always get sent off pre-season anyway!".

career move now, wouldn't it? I'm sure Fergie told him to go and suck some of his Russian boiled sweets and exercise his gob that way.

SATURDAY 4TH MARCH

A match day at home in Boothstown. In ze morning, Raphael came running in and said zat Chris Jointstrong of Dismal Palace had been caught smoking pot. Well, with ze state of zere pitch, I can promise he is ze only Palace person to have played on grass zis season. Isabella has had a craving for cheese puff balls - so we all sat down with zese and a box of after-eights to watch a bootleg video of Forrest Gump. "Is this the one about Stan Cauliflower?" asked Isabella. "No - zat is Forest Grump". Raphael had hold of ze teletext and kept checking ze score from Old Trafford. It was like watching ze stock price change on ze city exchange it kept going up so fast. And, I can tell you, ze price of Cole definitely went up. When it finished at 9-0, Isabella said with a wry smile: "Do you want an After Nine?" We all held hands and danced round the room singing: "Nine-nil without Cantona, Nine-nil without Cantona!"

MONDAY 6TH MARCH

Training with ze lads - ze were all joking saying, would I get in ze team ahead of Choccy. I took it good humouredly and reminded zem to say hello to ze advertising hoardings at Selhurst Park tomorrow. Fergie was in one of his good moods but I noticed zat he was handing out nose protectors to ze whole squad. "You never know with Vinny Groans", he said.

TUESDAY 7TH MARCH

Raphael and me listened to ze United game at Wimbledon on Radio Five. I could not believe it when ze said zat Hans Seger Mega Bribe had dropped ze ball for Brucey Bonus to score with only six minutes left. We were so excited zat we danced up and down in ze kitchen singing ze Teddy Bears picnic to Isabella's pregnant belly.

THURSDAY 9TH MARCH

Nipped in to do some training with ze Under-sevens. We played for ze Arnold Sidebottom Cup - which was very ornate and pretty. I had to tell one of zem not to lift it up, however, as Clayton Blackhead used to vomit in it after drinking all his lager and toffee apple liqueurs.

SUNDAY 12TH MARCH

United reached ze semi-finals of ze FA Cup after beating Queens in ze Park Rangers 2-0. I am glad zat we didn't sign zat Lesbian Ferdinand - someone should have told him Deaf Papa Cantona's old saying: "Shit or get off the pot!". Ze QPR manager, Gay Wilkins, makes me laugh. "He is so gullible," Fergie once told me, "zat he buys hair restorer from a bald barber". Lee NotsoSharpe did one of his daft dances after scoring, trying to do an Elvis Presley impression. "Lame, man," said Raphael, wrinkling his eyebrows.

MONDAY 13TH MARCH

All ze talk is of footballers taking "bungs". At first I thought zey said dung - and I wondered if zat would explain Bruce Grabbalot's bad breath. It is such an amazing story...imagine bribing goalkeepers to let in goals when you've already got Dave Beasant in ze world. I avv been a bit concerned at ze moment because of ze state of Gail Tilsley's marriage. I think she must borrow Barry Venison's hairpiece.Oh...I almost forgot to say...what a surprise zat John Flashanu was linked with corruption. Surely zat big Nancy boy is whiter than white.

TUESDAY 14TH MARCH

Zere is a strange atmosphere in ze dressing room. Ze players seem to be lacking confidence. I picked up my mail at ze club and zere were 7000 letters asking me to please stay. Andrex Andrei said he'd had loads as well but Fergie shouted out: "You've only had one - and that was from your Mum!"

WEDNESDAY 15TH MARCH

Watched Sportsnight with Isabella. She is getting so big now she looks a bit like a stranded beetle with her legs in ze air when she tries to get up from ze sofa.Ze Reds were pretty dire against Tottenham FlopSpurs. Andy Colenotdole missed a chance zat Raphael would have scored and Brucey Bonus trying to contain Jurgen Divesman was like watching Derek Wilton use ze Milemuncher. We are starting to look a bit anxious and I only wish I could be out zere.

SATURDAY 18TH MARCH

Ze family walked down to ze corner 7-11 shop to place ze National Lottery bet. Raphael says zat if he wins ze millions he will pay for a new sports centre in Manchester and for someone to give David Maynevergetinzeteam football lessons. Poor old David - when someone told him you had to choose six numbers for ze lottery, he thought zat meant numbers one to six, and cannot understand why he still has not won.

SUNDAY 19TH MARCH
A bad result for ze lads at Liverpool. Fergie hates going zere at ze best of times. Don't think I will leave a message on his ansaphone tonight. Ze commentator called Neil Pillock a contact defender - I agree: he's all con and no tact. Andrex Andrei has been talking to ze East Aberdeen Bugle saying zat he would like to play in Scotland. Well, he is certainly replacable and he might feel differently after being kicked up in ze air all season by Porridge-eating ginger bearded men. Raphael got told off tonight for using ze C word. 'Never mention Crystal Palace in this house' said Isabella.

TUESDAY 21ST MARCH
Collected Raphael from his private school in Worsley. I asked him what he had been studying and he said zey had been learning about dinosaurs - he said zat ze Stegasaurus was a big lumbering creature who couldn't move very quickly and fell over a lot. A little tear fell from ze corner of my eye and Raphael said: 'Why are you crying, Papa?' 'Your description made me think of all ze things I am missing not playing against Arsenal and Donkey Adams tomorrow night. Zat evening Isabella asked me what I thought would happen at ze court case. "It will probably go to a replay, my petite sunflower. Zese petty little bureaucrats are notoriously right wing and small-minded. Ze would bring back hanging if ze could - especially to Frenchmen. Fuck zem, my dear. I shall not even wear a tie, now I think about it".

WEDNESDAY 22ND MARCH
Zere were 14 messages on ze ansaphone. Zis has to be a record. Two were from Fergie, who kept talking about a kilt. When will zat man ever learn. My brother Joel rang up - and zere was even one from Denis Bogman Irwin telling me zat he wanted to know if my movements were affected by ze stress. Zen my lawyer, David Poole, rang to say zat I was not to sing any Pogues songs in ze court and to look serious when I pretended to be sorry for kicking zat little piece of crap. Zen Incey rang and said: "Eric, old China. Come clubbing tonight, we're all going daaan this great joint in Covent Garden. I met up with Incey after ze game. He said ze lads had pissed it against Arsenal - but he said zat Ian Fight Fight Fight was said to

have punched Brucey Bonus in ze tunnel at half-time. Apparently Sparkey had joked afterwards zat it was lucky Brucey Bonus hadn't brought his old gran there because Ian Fight Fight Fight might have been tempted to spit near her. Ze Browns Club was quite nice and zere was Don Perignon a plenty flowing. Some other players were in zere. Phil Scab of Liverpus with some old slapper hanging on to his arm. Paul Gasleak came over and said: "What have you and Incey got in common with a sardine? - You'll both end up in the can!". "Piss off fatso" I said. Zen Incey suggested we went to ze Emporium to see Prince or Symbol as he's known. He was absolute turtle shit. He was very rude too - he kept sticking his tounge out. Still we got nicely pissoired up and rolled back into ze Croydon at 5am! We walked into ze hotel foyer arm-in-arm singing Jailhouse Rock.

THURSDAY 23RD MARCH

Great balls of Sacha Distel! I'd only had three hours of sleep and zere was an urgent phone call from lawyer, Maurice Wethimself, saying: "Get up Eric, you're in Court in ten minutes". My head was thumping like a great big bass drum. I put on my blue jacket and a T-shirt. Ze moment I walked into Croydon Magistrates Court I knew zere would be trouble. What a case of mistaken nonentity one old bag was. All glass pearls, blue rinse hair and knotted pubes, she kept talking like a wizened old school maam. Zese petty little officials are no better zan ze seagull droppings on a Montpellier window sill. My mind kept wandering as one woman chundered on. "Did she get zat face blocking a kick?" I whispered to Incey. His case had been postponed and he was still humming Bee Gees hits from ze night before. Ze court heard my statement about what zat little weasel said, calling me a fucking cheat and mother-fucker and telling me to go back to France. "I was taking his advice," I whispered to my solicitor - "Ze quickest route was straight ahead and through zat little fuck pig!".

Zen zere were a lot more waffling speeches and one old prat started saying how I was an example to children and should be made to suffer. What a crazy world. Henry Pissinger bombed ze life out of millions of Cambodians and got ze Nobel Peace Prize, I kick a man with a 1970's haircut and ze want to send me to prison for two weeks. When zis Mrs Preach had finished I gave her one of my withering looks and said ze old Cantona curse: "May your piss always come out stinging like vinegar". By ze look of her craggy old face, zis may be happening already. Zen I was taken down to ze cells while my lawyers went for ze appeal. Zis fat prison guard came by after an hour carrying, with dirty fingernails, a bowl of lumpy yellow sick-looking liquid with what looked like a piece of old physio's sponge speckled with Nicky Butthead's blackheads. "Gaard bless you Mr Cantona...this is a fine English delicacy called Spotted Dick". "Take zis shit away", I shouted, "I have heard about ze sort of prisoners who swallow dick!" Zen, after sixteen games of Eye Spy with a man who'd been arrested for urinating in ze Mayor of Croydon's hat, I was free to leave. I rushed back up to Manchester and kissed and kissed my Isabella. Zat poisonous old battle axe had spouted on about family values but had wanted to jail me and make my seven-months pregnant wife suffer. Raphael rushed to ze door and said: "Daddy, you'll never believe it...".

'What?'

"Alex Ferguson let himself be pictured wearing a kilt".

We all fell asleep exhausted.

FRIDAY 24TH MARCH

Caught up on my washing with a special batch of Chat zat my mother had sent me. "Keep your smalls clean," she had written. "They haven't been small for years" I joked to Isabella.

SATURDAY 25TH MARCH

Ze papers are full of ze speculation zat I will pissoir off. Zat is why I knew what was happening when ze phone rang and someone said: "Bonjourno, Inter Milan President Massimo Moratti here, Monsieur Cantona. Come and play for us and I will pay you 75 million pesetas a year" - 'You can stop right now, Incey, you dopey Cockney - lira is ze Italian currency'. "Aww shit mate - good spot" Incey joked before ringing off. Still it gave me a good idea...perhaps I will do my Italian voice and start ringing up Martin Deadwood and Fergie!

MONDAY 27TH MARCH

British summer time certainly started in style...with snow. "Well, ze climate is certainly a big reason to stay," joked Isabella.

THURSDAY 30TH MARCH

A tense day at home. 'Papa if you do have to go to jail, will you try and break out?' said Raphael. "Don't worry, little Raphael, I have seen ze episodes of Porridge. I will just keep my snout clean, do my bird, and play by ze rules". Save zat shit for tomorrow I heard him say under his breath as he skipped off. 'Do you really think zey will jail you Eric?' said Isabella."Ze haven't got ze balls" I told her. I am already thinking up ze best way of rubbing ze press noses in it afterwards.

FRIDAY 31ST MARCH

Back to ze Saaarf London - land of bullet-headed men and women in mohair mini skirts - and zat's only ze legal profession. Ze Judge at ze Appeal Court was a top notch man. He said zat ze normal Home Office rulings had been ignored iand zat even a stoic would have kicked zat little prick. Ze court was full of Reds - all wearing zere kilts. People were handing me poems and scarves. When ze Judge sentenced me to 120 hours Community Service saying I would have to teach backward people how to play football I thought he meant I'd get the Manchester Shitty manager's job. Isabella rang me at ze court and said it was her nice polka dot tie zat had impressed ze judge. She also said zat Deaf Cousin Cantona had faxed her and said don't forget the sardine saying. Went to ze press conference. I don't know what is worse - A petit cell with a bucket of slops in ze corner or ze rancid odour of a room full of fat sweaty old hacks. I said to zem: "When seagulls follow a trawler, it is because they think sardines will be thrown into the sea". Zat load of old merde baffled them. When I got home Raphael said: "Mon pere, you got the seagull joke wrong, you were supposed to mention what ze sexually frustrated magistrate does with seagulls". 'Go to bed Raphael'. Isabella came down with a big grin saying, "I've brought you a nice bottle of claret and I've rented a video of 'The Fugitive". Sacre Bleu - her hormones must be affecting her sense of humour.

SATURDAY 1ST APRIL

Raphael is such a cheeky little rascal. He found our little Picasso telephone book and looked up Fergie's number. Zis was under N - for Nesbitt. Zen he rang him and pretended to be Massimo Moratti. When he could hear all zese choking sounds he said: "Merry April Fool's from ze Cantona boys!". Isabella came in with a copy of ze Guardian and said: "I wonder how zat dried up woman feels zis morning after reading about legal incompetence". Zen we all ate our bowls of Chocolate Coco-pops and played a game of Monopoly. Naturally, I was first to get ze get out of jail free card. Isabella said - 'With your luck, ma little Eric chicadee, your probation officer will turn out to be a Red and you'll spend 120 hours drinking Red wine'. Zat is enough for now. I've seen ze worst side of stinking English hypocrisy in ze last few months. Be free.

"When the Seagulls follow the trawler it is because they think Sardines will be thrown into the Sea"

SARDINES

RED NEWS 1996

THURSDAY 6TH APRIL

Zere is nothing on ze television tonight so we decided to watch ze Zis Is Your Life on Jimmy Hill zat I taped recently. But we had to turn it off because Raphael had his 3-D glasses on, and everytime Jimmy Hill moved his head towards the camera, Raphael jumped back thinking zat a giant piece of French bread was coming at him.

SATURDAY 8TH APRIL

I avv arrived back in France for a break from all zis nonsense in England. I think zat zere are more words written about me zan any other person in Britain. I think it will be like Gazza. Zey help drive him away so zey can claim huge expenses to go abroad and still write about him.

SUNDAY 9TH APRIL

I dreamt I was John Sadlesore of ze Scum newspaper. I woke up covered in urine, reeking of alcohol after dreaming zat I could only get an erection looking at pictures of Brian Clough's scabs. Ze horror! Whilst I was busy painting another masterpiece, Raphael listened to ze FA Cup semi-final on ze radio. He said zat it was the safest place to watch Iain Dowie. He said zat Pally had been booked - now ze world really is going mad. Zere were also reports of ze fans fighting. Zis I don't need.

MONDAY 10TH APRIL

Ahh - a lovely French day. A load of bread, a glass of wine and not a reporter in sight.

WEDNESDAY 12TH APRIL

Ze lads won through to another Cup Final. As expected ze Dismal Palace were easily swept aside - although ze lads were all a bit subdued. Roy Keane As Mustard got involved in a stamping incident - allzough I must say his technique could do with a bit of work after zat ugly Darren Colegate kicked his ankle.

GOOD FRIDAY

A quiet day in ze Cantona household. We avv moved out of ze little house in Worsley and into a hotel complex zat resembles something out of Cell Block 10. Isabella is bigger by ze day. We both now think zat we are going to have a girl - I think zat we will call her Cautious. Zat has a very nice ring about it. Cautious Cantona - and so true to our natures.

SATURDAY 15TH APRIL

Ze lads won at Leicester City. Mark Drooper was zere best player, said Incey, but he looks like one of zose retards who live in ze Appelachian mountains playing ze banjo. Andy Colenotdole scored for ze lads...ze first goal he has scored in a while. He will come good zough. Maybe. Perhaps. You never know.

MONDAY 17TH APRIL

A terrible goalless draw with ze ze Chelseasick. I did not listen to it, but ze newsagent told me zat United had about as much chance of winning as I did of ze lottery. Sacre bleur! Manchester Shitty beat ze Blackbum. Zat is good news but it does show zat ze Premiership is up ze spout zis season.

TUESDAY 18TH APRIL

Started ze community service training. About 200 desperate fat hacks were trying to get pictures. All ze locals were making money by renting zem ladders knowing zat ze walls of ze Cliff were too high anyway. I wrote out a detailed training plan for ze kids, which said: "Kick ball around - zen sign autographs for 2 hours".
It was nice - all ze kids were enthusiastic - and zere coaches were even more so. I think I will take my Sony Walkman in with me next time.

WEDNESDAY 19TH APRIL

Another phone call from ze lawyer. He said zat Inter Milan had increased zere offer to £35,000 a week, six jars of Dolmio pasta sauce a month and as many Armani socks as I want. United responded zough and said zat if I stay I will never have to share a room with Roy Keane As Mustard ever again. Now zat is what I call an offer.

THURSDAY 20TH APRIL

Raphael called me to see ze lame Ryan Giggsy Corns-on-toe burger advert on ze television. Zat lad is so smarmy in it zat he looks like he is in a party political broadcast. Whatever next? Bogman doing blue loo adverts - Steve Brucey Bonus in a corset promotion and Andrex Andrei in a Rennie settle-your-stomach ad?

MONDAY 24TH APRIL

A big meeting with Fergie and Martin Deadwood. Fergie was keen on me to stay, I think, judging from ze way he got down on his knees and sang - "Buddy can you spare me a game". Zey offered me more money and a house in leafy Cheshire with a remote control cat flap. I need time to think. It is not ze club - I still love zat - but how many more cropped haired black jacketed cretins are out zere?

THURSDAY 27TH APRIL

I rang ze "BT Call-back" number of ze phone and it said zat it was a direct line to ze Sports Desk of ze Daily Mirror. "Raphael", I shouted, "Come here". When I asked him what he'd been up to, ze little rascal said he had been pretending to be an Inter Milan spokesman saying zat I was definitely leaving United. "What are you going to do Papa?". He said zen winked as if he didn't know.

Zen Incey rang up and said: "Eric, if you stay, even I will call you the Guvnor". "Zat is ok, Incey wincey...but Roy Keane As Mustard has to wash my car"."Done mate" he said.

Zen I rang up Fergie and said: "I have made my final decision...I will not keep you waiting a moment longer. Not a second more will I keep ze news from you...Oh ze alarm on ze microwave has just gone off".

(One Minute Later)

"Are you ok, Alex? I think you are making zose choking noises again...Ok. The decision is zat...Just a second mon amie, Isabella needs her pillow propping up".

(Two Minutes Later)

"Ok zen...For double ze dosh and a year's supply of Pampers nappies, I will stay at ze greatest club in ze world. It's ok, Alex, you can stop weeping for joy".

Zen I told Isabella zat zey would give ze news to David Meekshall Inherit-the-story and it would be known today. Zen her and Raphael started giggling. "What is zis laughter for?" I said. "You know full well, my little Eric chicadee zat I want our next child to be born in England and Raphael would have put arsenic in your red wine if you'd left Old Trafford". I turned away pretending to be in a huff but secretly laughed. It was a funny game to keep up for three months. Oh merde! I forgot to insist zat zey sell David Mayneverbeheardofagain as part of ze deal.

FRIDAY 28TH APRIL

Had to get up early to meet ze scabby seagulls at ze Old Trafford Europa suite. Fergie was doing a little jig when I arrived. For once I did not joke and said zat I knew how much he had done for me. Ze press conference was dull as dishwater. I wore my deckchair outfit to muck up zere lenses and just answered a few pissoir poor questions.

Martin Deadwood wasn't on ze ball as he told zem I was signing to stay until 1988!

How will you handle ze pressure, "Easily", I said. Zen I joked zat I had to go to training to get fit for my next game in October. "Now if zat had been Brian McClard" joked Incey, "I'd have believed it...It would take him about six months to lose his waistline". Ze atmosphere in training was brilliant. Ze lads all welcomed me back and I even got shouted at by Peter Streudal. I'm home again. Now ze future is looking good. Went to bed and felt Isabella's big belly. Not long, now, my sweet pea. "If it is a boy", she joked, "Shall we call it Matthew?".

SUNDAY 14TH MAY

Raphael came running in to tell me zat Blackbum Rovers were Champions. United had drawn at ze Wets Ham when Andy Colenotdole had done his impression of Superman - just after someone has stuck a great lump of Kryptonite round his neck. "What are you talking about, son?" "Well, Papa, I mean zat he could not have hit Roseanne's arse with a 12-bore shotgun if she'd been tap dancing on his window sill". Zey showed ze highlights of ze game on French TV later on and it was frantic, manic stuff in ze last 20 minutes. In fact ze United players were all over ze place like a mad woman's shit, as Blind Uncle Burgundy used to say.

MONDAY 15TH MAY

I played a game of football today...and scored. I was playing for Michel Platini's charity match to raise money to fight ze drug abuse. I wore a No.10 Merson shirt for ze warm-up. I heard zat Graham Smelly of ze FA pissoired in his pants when he learned zat I had played and zere was nothing he could do about it because FIFA had said it was OK. Actually, it was only ze doorman at ze FIFA headquarters who said yes - but he had such a big impressive moustache zat no-one wanted to argue with him.

THURSDAY 18TH MAY

Over for a quick visit to ze lads, who are staying at a hotel in Windsor before ze Cup Final. It is funny but ze lads don't seem very up for ze game. Giggsy is trying to get fit by putting bags of frozen bubble and squeak on his thigh's while Incey must be very dehydrated judging from ze amount of bubbly fluid he is taking in... Andrex Andrei isn't talking to anyone because someone joked zat his hernia problem was a result of straining on ze loo trying to pass all zat red cabbage he eats. Ze only one who seems happy is Nicky Butthead, who keeps winking at ze boss.

SATURDAY 20TH MAY
What a pissoir poor day. Great balls of Sacha Distel, we were merde. It is funny watching a game from ze red paddy seats at Wembley - ze make your legs sweaty. Ze whole team played like frogs turds except for Giggsy. Lee NotsoSharpe was so pathetic zat I thought he must have swallowed 600 downers and eaten a 4-course meal before going on. Everton were nothing special but I think zat Crewe would have beaten us. Ze boss did not say anything after ze game, but he kept mumbling to Kiddo: "Aye, and he can pack his fehkin bags". I expect he was talking about ze people going on holiday.

WEDNESDAY 24TH MAY
I celebrate my 29th birthday today.

THURSDAY 1ST JUNE
I avv been doing some filming while we wait for ze birth of our child. Ze lads will never believe it when I tell zem zat I will be in a real cinema film release called Happiness Is In The Meadow. And no, it is not ze Meadow zat Shrewsbury played at. I am playing a rugby player called Lionel who falls in love. Of course, rugby is a very popular game in ze far south of France, far more zan football. I never liked it zough. All zat groping of men's testicles in ze scrum. I saw enough of zat in Sergeant Wilko's office at Leeds.

MONDAY 5TH JUNE
I avv become a father again. Zis time to a lovely girl called Josephine. Raphael keeps running round saying: "Not tonight" but zat joke is wearing a bit thin as it is about as old as Gay Wilkins.

TUESDAY 20TH JUNE
Incey Wincey is leaving ze club. Ze boss has said someone close to ze player had been touting for a move to Inter Milan for months. We had all thought zat it was just coincidence zat he was always wearing a blue and white striped football shirt and black shorts of late. Roy Keane As Mustard didn't look too down as he has already grabbed Ince's "I am The Guv'nor" headed notepaper. All ze press were saying what a loss it would be to United but it was strange to hear Bogman's reaction: "Oh yeah we'll all miss a big mouthed, do-nothing, who seems to prefer a massage to training, rarely scores

and slags us all off on and off the pitch". Oh no, I told him, don't worry...Lee is staying.

FRIDAY 30TH JUNE

Kenny Dogleash has quit as ze big wig of Blackbum and ze job has gone to his assistant Ray Halfwit. I was very pleased about zis because it actually solved one of ze great mysteries of English football for me...who ze fuck was zat man in ze bobble hat who used to shout dementedly from ze Blackbum dug out. To be honest, I add thought he was one of zose local unfortunates zey release from a home each Saturday to get some fresh air and integrate with ze community.

WEDNESDAY 12TH JULY

George Graham has been suspended for a year after definitely not meaning to take a bung. Mind you, just for buying John Jenson alone he should have been banned for zat long.

THURSDAY 20TH JULY

I was half expecting a call from Joe Royleteaparty today asking me what to do when you have a Ukrainian stuck to a large shiny bit of silverware! Let me explain. Andrex Andrei has bogged off to Everton for £5 million. But ze silly turd allowed himself to be photographed holding ze FA Cup...not ze best way of thanking ze United fans for all zere loyal support. Anyway, back to my joke - I half expected Joe to ring because after he was given the Cup someone said: "You can pass it back, now Andrei" and he didn't know ze meaning of ze word. Fergie was storming, of course. Saying zat ze ungrateful little shit had been earning six bob a week and as much red cabbage soup as he could eat before he came to Old Trafford and now he was wanting £20,000 a week. Expect Bogman to imitate Fred Astaire on his ankles next season when zey come to Old Trafford. Ze deal will probably run into trouble, anyway, because a 23-stone money lender from ze Black Sea owns 19.48 per cent of Andrex Andrei including his appendix and his right ear - and ze fat man always wants paying.

TUESDAY 25TH JULY

Had a practice match against Emmerdale. Ze boss said zat I was not to worry when I said was zis okay with ze FA. He just winked. You could tell it was just a training match by ze fact zat we had a top FIFA referee, two linesmen and only a few new players with names like Romario, Bebeto, Klinsmann and Boli playing! With a minute to go, zere were suddenly 18 substitutions made - and when I went to scratch my balls I suddenly realised zere was a photographer taking pictures. "How did he get in?" I asked one of ze lads. 'Oh ze Boss said it would certainly put a hot pepper up Graham Smelly's arse if he woke up to see pictures of Monsieur Eric playing football again...' Isabella has just asked me if zis is ze truth. Of course not. It was like a park kickabout with 48 players, one-goal-and-in for ze goalkeeper's and a set of old adidas bags as ze goalposts...Some competitive match.

WEDNESDAY 26TH JULY

Back in ze swing of ze pre-season training. Paul Nosey Parker is all chirpy because he hasn't pulled his hamstring for four days. He shouted out to all ze lads: "If Tony Adams, Paul Merson and Ray Pizza Parlour are in a car, who is driving?". "Don't know" shouted the Neville Brothers. "A policeman" said Nosey Parker. I am starting to feel a bit excited about ze season. I avv done my community bird and haven't felt like doing a kung-fu kick for months. Although Isabella has taken all my Bruce Lee videos back to France - so maybe she is suspicious! Giggsy shouted out zat I should get a Steve Brucey Bonus video - you certainly don't see him lifting his legs very high. Ze Skipper took ze joke well - but zen again it is difficult for him to catch Giggsy in his zimmer-frame.

THURSDAY 27TH JULY

Training was good again - but ze lads are off on tour to Malaysia tomorrow. We were all talking about Sparky who has started well at Chelsea. Pally is crapping himself at ze thought of facing him next year. "Yeah, he won't score but he'll certainly knock you sideways" piped up Nicky Butthead. Nobody laughed. He must be careful not to be too much of an upstart, something David Maynotgetinzeteamforzesecondseason running reminded him of when he said: "Here, I make the unfunny jokes around this place!". Ze conversation zen turned on to mobile phones. It seems zat me and Brian McClard and Gary Welshrabbit and ze Neville Brothers are ze only ones without them. Welshrabbit has dropped his zough. "What about Bogman, surely he hasn't got one?", I said. "Err, yes, Monsieur Eric...in case I am ever stuck in a toilet". Denis Bogman Irwin has been busy zis summer writing lots of letters to the Prime Minister. When he read zat ze were closing ze Cones Hot-line he wrote to John Major suggesting a toilet hot-line. If you ever find zere is no toilet paper in a public bog zen you ring ze toilet hot-line. "You need a holiday" said Fergie, who was hiding in ze shower all ze time (just for ze banter he said later). Zen Lee NotsoSharpe said to David Maynotgetinzeteamforzesecondseason running: "Have you got a mobile?" - but before he could answer, Brucey Bonus shouted out "A mobile home", zen Pally added: "It's ze only mobile thing about him". We all roared. I shall miss ze banter next week.

SUNDAY 6TH AUGUST
Isabella is gone and I am right down in ze dumps. I am stuck in ze Novaltina Hotel eating zere plastic chicken chasseur again. Ze only engossing thing on ze telly is Coronation Street and Match Of Ze 70's. Zey showed Kiddo going apeshit with a referee in one game last week...I shall avv to mention zat. Zen I checked teletext and it said zose turds from ze FA were going to investigate ze training match I had against Rochdale. As if I avvn't got enough on my plate worrying about Steve McDonald running off with Vicky's money. Incidentally I must make a note to ask if he reminds any of ze lads of Lee NotsoSharpe. Talking of plates, I won ze East-Hartlepool Supporters' Club Player of December 1994 award, and zey sent me some poxy ornamental plates...But ze only thing we use them for is to keep Raphael's snails on zem.

MONDAY 7TH AUGUST
Woke up in a right stinker of a mood. I rang Inter Milan and said: "I am leaving Manchester United and you can avv me next season. I am sick to my stomach of ze sweaty small minded obese fuckwits who are in all ze positions of power here. I am open to offers and zat is my final word". Zen when I put ze phone down, Raphael rang and said: "Papa, I can't wait to see you play against Liverpool next October". Sacre Bleu! I tried to ring Inter Milan back but I could only get ze Italian club call line and it was all foreign. I went into see Martin Deadwood to test ze water. "Some great things are destined to come apart" I said. "Take That, Lyle Lovett and Julia Roberts, Mike and Bernie Winters...But there not zem!" He just ignored my joke and started saying: "But the shares will tumble. The dividends will fall, locusts, pestilence". He was foaming at ze mouth at zis point and I decided it was best to leave. Zey put out a statement. Later, back at ze hotel playing solitaire and eating my individual toad-in-ze-hole TV dinner for one, zere was a knock on ze door. Fergie, red in ze face and with a hankie at ze ready, spent 2 hours talking so fast zat I could not understand him. I think he was asking me to stay. But he

interrupted ze Monday night edition of ze Street so I think I may have still seemed in a bad mood.

TUESDAY 8TH AUGUST

A knock on ze door at 8am. I thought it was ze young porter with my apricot jam and croissants but it was Fergie. He looked like shit and said he hadn't slept. I said zat I was in a much better mood and had changed my mind and would stay. He leapt in ze air and yelled: "Yes, yes, yes...What did I say zat made you change my mind!".
"Nothing...but I can't get Coronation Street in Marseilles and Raphael would probably stick knitting needles in me if we left England - he has made some nice friends". Zen Fergie's face fell. "What is wrong, Boss?". "Well, I thought it would take longer for you to decide to stay and I was going to fly to Paris...it got me out of a social event with a wife's relative. He's the most boring arsehole in ze world". "No problem. Just say you are on a mission to keep me - fly out and we'll have a good meal in Paris. I will show you what we mean by ze good cuisine. Not your British version of saggy old dried out meat and vegetables zat avv been boiling for three weeks".

WEDNESDAY 9TH AUGUST

A great night. Fergie was as happy as Larry and I was all pleased-but who is zis Larry? Larry Hagman? I don't think he can be pretty happy the state his liver is in at the moment. I'm glad it wasn't liver on ze menu but fish. We eat at L'aime Louis, I think it's named after Louis Armstrong - brother of Chris. We were ze only people zere - but the waiter looked suspiciously like Danny Wallace. Fergie had even bought me one of zose little bronze Eiffel Towers which I managed to drop in a bin as we said goodbye. I am off to a christening in Marseilles and zen back for training on Monday.

THURSDAY 10TH AUGUST

My brother Joel rang - when I asked him if he'd been surprised by it all, he just said: "No, once ze Daily Mirror said you were leaving I knew you'd be at Old Trafford next season!".

FRIDAY 18TH AUGUST

Ze new season is about to start. All ze football pull outs are showing ze new players - Stan Cauliflower, David Splatt, Bert Camp, Rude to Pullit in Public, Chris Jointstrong. I don't think zat we are quite ready for ze start. Andy Colenotdole's calves are still a bit achey - zough he says zis does zough he says zis does not stop him breakdancing at ze clubs in ze Tottenham area of North Cockneyeelpieland London sometimes. I am sitting in ze stands for ze game.

SATURDAY 19TH AUGUST

What a difference Paul Nosey Parker made. Strength, cohesion, covering and timing. He had none of zese. We were completely overrun by ze Aston Vanilla. Peter Streudal in goal was flapping about like a wind mill and we looked like a team of little lost boys. After ze game Fergie asked my opinion. It was "golemstrumpy", I said. "What does that mean, Jimmy", he said in his Rab C.Nesbitt voice. "Well it was two pounds of shit in a one pound bag...very messy".

SUNDAY 20TH AUGUST

All ze papers have written United off - and given Blackbum Rovers ze great write ups. Mark my words, zat shower will be found out zis season.

WEDNESDAY 23RD AUGUST

Old Trafford is strange at ze moment. Bits of ze ground are missing, zere are barely 30,000 people inside and ze atmosphere is about as lively as a Manchester Shitty glee club. Ze boys did better tonight. David Beckenhambypass was not afraid of Julian Dicks (now zat is one name zat could be appropriate) even zough Dicks looked like zat poor unfortunate paper boy back in Auxerre who'd been hit on ze head by a combine harvester. Paul Schoolboys was very good and his shiny carrot head was very distinctive in ze floodlights. In Australia, anyone with red hair is automatically called Blue...so zat will be my secret nickname for him now. Roy Keane as Mustard did well for ze game. Gary Neville Brothers showed me ze big gash in his leg caused by zat mad Double Dutchman Marco Beefboogers. Steve Brucey Bonus was so angry I thought he was going to shove a big clog where ze sun does not shine. Andy Colenotdole was all happy as he had lasted a whole 20 minutes without once singing an Abba song on ze pitch.

FRIDAY 25TH AUGUST

All ze lads were reading about ze love life of Lesbian Ferdinand. He may have been having ze old glamour sex, licking champagne off women's breasts, but he will have to approach things differently in Newcastle. "Eh canny boy, just splash a bit of Newky Brown on ma tits and dive in pet" they'll say.

SATURDAY 26TH AUGUST

Great balls of Sacha Distel! We beat ze Dons quite easily. I think ze Wombles would avv given us a harder game. Vinny Groans was strutting about early on trying to frighten Nicky Butthead but Roy Keane as Mustard soon showed who was boss. Andy Colenotdole scored a cracker of a goal...zat is what I call nifty feet. Fergie was a happy chappy after ze game. He even gave me a wink when he was walking along with Martin Deadwood. Perhaps I will get another pay rise. Ze players have been joking about ze fact zat I earn so much money but do not want ze trappings of wealth. "Well, look at all ze money Roy makes", I said, "and he still walks around in shell suits".

SUNDAY 27TH AUGUST

Raphael got out ze copy of True Lies from ze video shop at ze corner - Bert Ramsden's goggle Box Delights. I think zat Arnold Schwarzenegger better watch out...Manchester Shity will buy any big lump with a foreign name zese days. Paul Wince was making his debut for Inter Milan - somehow I bet zat Fergie was not watching Channel 4 zis afternoon.

MONDAY 28TH AUGUST

Fergie asked me whether I was going to the Earwax Park to see ze Reds play Blackbum. "Are you kidding?" I said. "And miss seeing ze look on Alan Shearenvy's face when zey are beaten again?". How could a shower of such shit have won ze Championship. Zey make Sergeant Wilko's title winners look like ze Brazil of old. Graeme Le Sick was as niggly as ever and quite rightly got booked for a blatant dive to try to win a penalty. Roy Keane as Mustard, on ze other hand, was ze victim of a gross miscarriage of justice when he was booked for falling over one of Colin Henpecked's big sideburns. Lee NotsoSharpe, who now looks more and more like one of ze background figures in One Flew Over Ze Cuckoos Nest had equalised, David Beckenhambypass scored a fluffy little chip of a goal. It was great to see zem all troop off. Me and Kiddo were singing: "You're going down with ze City". I saw Kenny Dogleash and said: "Well it looks like you perfected your old Liverpool trick - getting out just before an ageing and overpraised side is found out". Zere was lots of jolly singing on ze coach home but David Maynotgetinzeteamforzesecondseasonrunning was not joining in for some reason.

THURSDAY 31ST AUGUST

Another good practice game at ze Cliff, zis time against Blackpool Rock. Zey were nifty and I shall bet on zem to win ze 2nd division title. I scored a cracking volley and Andy Colenotdole, who'd crossed ze ball, ran over and said: "Sweet, my man, sweet". I think zat boy eats out at restaurants too often.

SATURDAY 2ND SEPTEMBER

I bet zat Graham Smelly was pissing in his pants again today. A Premiership-free-weekend- so one less to ban Monsieur Cantona from.

MONDAY 4TH SEPTEMBER

So we avv buried Ivy Tilsley. Old, cantankerous, drunk-sodden, argumentative and spiteful. It sounds as if she should have been a football reporter for a tabloid.

WEDNESDAY 6TH SEPTEMBER

France won 10-0 against Azerbaijan. What a great result but it has been a shocking week to be a Frenchman. "Raphael and Joespehine", I told my kids: "Today we are all Northerners". Zis is because ze French government has stupidly been doing ze nuclear testing. Who do zey think is going to invade France, San Marino? Anyway if ze wanted to see a site that was totally devastated, unable to support proper human life and full of brain-damaged victims - ze could have just gone to Liverpool.

SATURDAY 9TH SEPTEMBER

Travelled with ze lads to Goodisgone Park. I sat next to ze lawyer Maurice Watsgoingon and Fergie. Bobby Charhead was behind us. I think I shall now call him Mr. Hefty Breath - he was snorting and puffing on ze back of my neck. Now it is not true zat ze lads all had a sweepstake on who would get Andrei Kanfuck off first. What a crying shame zat he was forced out of ze game by Lee LookingSharpeagain's flying tackle. I could not concentrate on ze next few minutes because of ze loud chuckling of a nearby Glaswegian. United did well to win - but Daniel Amataxi and Steve Brucey Bonus must be two of ze fatist old tubs of lards in ze game. Giggs scored an excellent winner, after all ze young lads had scampered about like puppies. How did we lose to zis team in ze FA Cup Final?

SUNDAY 10TH SEPTEMBER

Read of Gazza's naughty doings in ze News Of Ze Screws. Maybe he should have joined United, it would certainly have been more interesting than Brian McCLard.

MONDAY 11TH SEPTEMBER

Andrei Kanfuckoff has been spying for Roto Vulgarheads. He sent zem a video of United and zen rang to give ze low down on ze United players. He couldn't tell anyone anything of importance - he spent too much time with his head pointing down to ze turf to notice what ze style of play was like. Raphael has just come in with a joke. Ze are casting for a new movie about classical composers. Tom Hanks wanted to be Beethoven because of ze mystique. Bruce Willis wants to be Mozart. When ze asked Arnold Schwarzenegger he said..."I'll be Bach!". Ho ho!

TUESDAY 12TH SEPTEMBER

United's young pups got a great result - especially without me and Andy Colenotdole. Ze Roto Vulgerheads did not threaten much and ze only drawback was Roy Keane as Mustard falling over an old bit of Chernobyl fall out to hurt his hamstring. Still, it should mean I get to play in ze UEFA Cup zis season.

WEDNESDAY 13TH SEPTEMBER

Blackburn are shit and zey know ze are. What an embarrassment for English football zat zay are beamed around ze world as ze Champions of England. Alan Shearenvy did bugger all while Graeme Le Sick and Tim Flowerpot managed to gift a comedy goal. Raphael asked me if I would play Chris Suttonthebench. No, I said. He will never be more zan a glorified centre-half. Have you noticed zat he never kicks ze ball clearly, he always scuffs it. Scuff, scuff, scuff. And as for Ray Halfwit - he sold Newell cheaply when he was manager at Luton - and now he's preferring him to a £5m player. Zat's what I call management, huh!

SATURDAY 16TH SEPTEMBER

Another fantastic win by the Primary School XI. Ze new lad Terry Cookeymonster did one of my flicks - doesn't he know it's copyright. We're sure missing Brian McClard! Rovers are shit...perhaps they ARE going down with ze City! The long wait is nearly over.

MONDAY 18TH SEPTEMBER

I flew out to Paris for a meeting of ze World Footballers Glee Club with Diego Marijuana. I flew out on Air Nuke-em, ze new national airline of France. I had some of zose dry-roasted peanuts on ze flight. Why is it zat when you open zose packets, ze always smell of compressed farts? Zere were a lot of top European players zere including Cinzano Vialli and Sweden's Thomas Umbrollin. We all agreed zat footballers should be paid a lot of money and zat Beardo ze Weirdo was one of ze ugliest of our profession - alzough Diego said zat goalkeeper Rene Huggybear was an international rival. As I was leaving, Diego said zat when I got back to England I should give his regards to Peter Stiltonbreath. 'I shall tell him zat you were elected by a show of hands, mon amie - but I think zat he has other things on his mind, like things zat go bounce in ze night'.

TUESDAY 19TH SEPTEMBER

Ze kids really were absolutely fabulous on Saturday - beating Bolton Wanderland by ze three fine goals. Zere were so many kids in ze dressing room before ze game zat I thought Fergie was going to start showing ze Lion King and handing out Farleys Rusks. I sat on ze bench watching and I swear Fergie was purring when Terry Cookeymonster set up Giggsy for zat goal. Ze big mystery at ze moment is what has happened to David Maynotgetinzeteamforzesecondseasonrunning. We have decided zat he must be "doing a Lord Lucan" or "doing a Shergar". Judging by Brian McClard's figure zis week, I think he has been at ze After Eights again.

WEDNESDAY 20TH SEPTEMBER

Great balls of Sacha Distel! We were beaten by ze chocolate bar maker's team. Before ze game zere was too much complacency in ze dressing room. Kiddo just managed to stop one of ze players going out wearing his Sony Walkman. But - shock of shocks - we lost 3-0 to Pork City.

SATURDAY 23RD SEPTEMBER

Away to Sheffield Tuesday and it was one of ze most boring games in all my time at ze club. Curly Watts would avv add more chance of scoring. We were all talking about David Pillier of ze Arsewipe. He was found to avv smoked ze dope because he did not know what sort of cigarette it was when someone gave it to him at a party. Well if you believe zat zen you believe in Santa Claus coming down your chimney at Christmas; you believe in insurance premiums maturing; and you believe in Alan Ball's-Ups managerial skills!

SATURDAY 31ST SEPTEMBER
I don't know what sort of nightclubs some of ze young kids go to - but one of ze Neville Kids said zat one last night had a sign in ze toilets saying: "No rucking, fucking or sucking". Sacre Bleu - and I thought I was being daredevil taking Isabella to a Pret A Manger.

SUNDAY 1ST OCTOBER
Ze Glorious Day. Ze return of Monsieur Cantona. All my family was over for ze game. Joel came into ze dressing room to wish me luck and tell me not to worry. Neil Fattock looked like one of ze great pregnant cows zat Papa Pierre - ze one legged walnut grower - keeps on his farm in Marseille. Ze game was exciting. We scored early on when a pinpoint, state-of-ze-art genius pass reached Nicky Butthead who did one of my kung-fu kicks to get it in. Only later did I admit, after several beers, zat it was meant for Andy Colenotdole. I was pleased to score a penalty and I took ze piss out of Neil's stomach. Only Joel got ze joke about ze pregnant cow zough.

TUESDAY 3RD OCTOBER
On ze way to ze Pork City seocnd leg we were all laughing at Lee QuiteSharpeatzemoment's woolly jumper. 'Is your U-boat still in ze Manchester Ship canal?' said Brucey, because he did look like a German naval man from ze old black and white films. Brucey Bonus said he was taking his kids to see ze new Disney film Pocahontas. "I'm going to see ze adult version", joked Denis Bogman. "It stars Will Carling - it's called Pokeyourhighness!". I hate ze little Cup games. We were 2-0 up and should have thrashed ze Yorky bar team. In ze end Peter Streudal was doing his Rambo impressions and trying to invade their box. Fergie was furious when we went out, but his mood got better when Roy KeaneasMustard joked: "It could have been worse, boss, we could have drawn Fred West's favourite fixture". 'What's that?' we all said. "Bury - at home", he said. We all pissoired our pants laughing. So OJ Simpson got off. Perhaps he will get Michael Jackson to look after his kids. Ze world is mad.

THURSDAY 5TH OCTOBER
A lovely family day. Josephine is sitting up now - and we're only having to change nappies every second hour. "I can tell she's yours" said Isabella. 'How is zat?'. "Oh, just something in ze way she kicks

her legs".

SATURDAY 7TH OCTOBER

Sacre Bleu - after a good week of training, I was injured in ze reserve game against Leeds at Old Trafford. Zere were over 21,000 people zere. Zey must avv raked in a fortune at ze Megastore. And people wonder why United kept me!! Unfortunately, I hurt my knee and had to leave early.

TUESDAY 10TH OCTOBER

What a boring week. I avv been on ze treatment table getting my knee iced and zen massaged. After I used up all my note pads doing diagrams of ze game (I think it was a mistake telling Joel zis, as he zen rang up some magazine called Esquire again) and reading my Rothmans. Did you know zat Matthew Le Pissier's weight is 13 stone 8 pounds - zat is nearly two stone heavier zan three years ago. I think he must be eating too much of ze Jersey clotted cream.

SATURDAY 14TH OCTOBER

Great Balls of Sacha Distel! Manchester Shitty really lived up to zere name. We beat zem without me or Bogman, but I think we would avv won with Kiddo up front. Paul Schoolboys scored a nifty header about two foot off the ground and Andy Colenotdole could not avv hit Neil Fattock's arse with a frying pan. Ze worst miss of ze match, zough, was by Niall Queen. After ze game zere was zis high-pitched whine throughout ze backroom area. I thought one of ze boilers must be ready to explode, but zen Fergie said zat it was Alan Balls-Up giving a press conference. Fergie told us all zat he had said to him: "Alan, what's the difference between a cocktail stick and Manchester Shitty - a cocktail stick has two points".

FRIDAY 20TH OCTOBER

We all went down on ze coach to stay in Berkshire before ze game with Chelseasick. Fergie was talking with Ned Belly, who will help to protect me tomorrow. He says he was in ze SAS but when I questioned him closely it seems zat his combat record was a bit like Percy Sugden's. Not knowing how bright he is I said: "Let's see who can get ze most words out of your Christian name?". After three-quarters-of-an-hour, I said: "Well, I can only find 3...Ned, End and Den". "Oh, I only got Ned," he said. Lee NotsoSharpe was looking a bit glum but Paul Schoolboys was cheery - I wonder why?

Saturday 21st October

Sacre Bleu. What a performance. We wiped ze floor with Chelseasick. Ze only had two good players in zere whole team - and ze were both nearly 40. Still, I got ze better of Ruud Topullitinpublic and even nutmegged him. Sparky was good and gave Brucey Bonus a bit of a mauling - but I think he was a bit upset with Roy KeaneasMustard, who kept saying: "It's like you say, Sparky, there's only one way to go when you leave United - and that's down".

Zere seems to be a real swagger about Paul Schoolboys. At half-time he said zat it was nice to be congratulated - but could we stop calling him "carrot top". Anyway, he joked: "If you look closely at carrots, they've got green at the top". "Don't be such a trainspotter", Giggsy yelled at him. Zen Nicky Butthead said - "Heard about Fred West going down the pub. The barman says 'What can I get you?' - and Fred West says 'I could murder a few Tennants!'". We all went out to ze second half laughing. Ze game was not as good in ze second half - but we still came out on top. Sparky scored a goal, which was inevitable, and Giggsy scored a lovely solo one. Zere wasn't even much abuse for me.

Back home late evening to Isabella and ze family. We ate a box of Milk Tray as a treat and watched Match Of Ze Day. I did ze last call BT redial check on my phone - and it was an Italian number. Now zere's a surprise.

Sunday 22nd October

Joel rang me up to say - 'You'll never guess what? - I'm watching Dismal Palace vs Millwall on Carlton TV and ze Millwall fans are getting at ze home supporters by chanting: 'Ohh, Ahh Cantona'. My, it is a strange world...

Thursday 26th October

Raphael was a cheeky little Parisian monkey today. When he came back from school he said: 'Mum, why are we like Rose West's children? - Because we are always under your feet!'. Where do zey learn zese sick jokes? He made me watch Neighbours. Everytime someone is ill in Oz land zey say he is: "crook". I don't think I will say zat to Martin Deadwood, zough, he might get ze wrong idea.

Saturday 28th October

Zere was real tension in ze dressing room before ze game against Middlesbrothsoup. Ze boys did not want to lose to Robbo's team. Sadly, zey were going to be without Junewhitfieldo, ze little Brazilian

Imp as all ze old hacks call him. Robbo got a fantastic reception and Kiddo wet himself with anger when Lee NotsoSharpeagain said: 'I wonder if the tannoy man will announce him as ze next boss of Manchester United'. Ze match was pretty good. Giggsy was back to his best, teasing zem like a tempting woman does with black underwear when Frank Bough's in town. Zey had an aggravating big-nosed Scandanavian called Jan Forkhead and he was needling Roy Keane As Mustard. In ze end he exploded and chinned him. Ze boss was furious afterwards: 'Call zat a proper punch - it was a bloody powder puff!'. Ze best bright spot was zat Pally scored against his old club. "Well, we all know Walshy's no good at crosses", he said with a smirk.

SUNDAY 29TH OCTOBER

I add to do a promotion wiv a pop star in a field for ze advert monee. "It'll be alright...", said Isabella, "you're so televisual my little kicking donkey". I love zese pet names we all avv for our loved ones. When I got to ze field I thought zat zey had left a scraggly old scarecrow in ze middle. Zen it began walking towards me with greasy old red hair and outstretched hands. I offered him 20 pence but he said: "No, Monsieur Cantona, it's me - the famous pop star Red - you know, Mick Fucknell". He said he was from the some band called Pimply Red zat were top of ze charts. Frankly, I am not into zis pop music scene - I still like bopping to my Charles Asnovoice records. I don't think I want to see ze finished advert. Zen ze man, who seemed to have a personal hygiene problem, kept following me saying: "I'm a real fan. Honest, Really and truly I'm always in the VIP and Director's boxes. For almost every game. I've been going ever since we started being successful, honest I have". Ze only way I could get rid of him was to hail a taxi and dash off while he was peeing in ze bushes.

SATURDAY 4TH NOVEMBER

Back in ze Cockneyeelpie land for ze game at Bruce Riot's Arsewipe. We lost 1-0 and it was all Denis Bogman's fault. I think his mind was on Guy Fawkes night. Anyway, Fergie was really good afterwards saying in ze press conference zat it was ze first mistake he'd made in five years. "What about zat haircut last year" said Nicky Butthead. We all laughed but zen we started on zis Butthead. He is going to be up in ze courts accused of head-butting someone in Charlie Chin's Chinese palace. "It's lucky you didn't hit Ray Pizza Parlour in a pizza parlour...", joked Giggsy, "because the headline would have been

Butt butts Parlour in parlour". As he was putting on his socks we all started staring at each other saying: 'You want some? You want some?'. Zen Fergie came in and was not so happy to see us laughing. 'Do you realise you shower of shit lost?' I think zey are starting to talk about Andy Colenotdole in code because zey keep talking about barn doors. Ze worst thing of ze whole day was bumping into Nigel Warthogface in ze players area after ze game. He is so ugly. Paul Schoolboys nearly got into a fight when he told him zat it was time he took off his Halloween mask.

FRIDAY 17TH NOVEMBER
I avv been reading a new book about a colourful elephant called Elmer to baby Josephine. Isabella said to me: "Why are you bothering with clumsy big creatures with large ears - I would avv thought you get enough of zose at work!".

SATURDAY 18TH NOVEMBER
Ze lads put on a fabulous display against ze Saints of Southampton. Ze big nosed Matthew Le Pissier was not playing - but zen zat is nothing new for zis season. Giggs was at ze top of his form and scored but all round we really looked back to our best - even Andy Colenotdole scored with a header. We were disappointed not to see Bruce Grababung in ze goal. I wonder where he is now? We had a sweepstake in ze dressing room at half-time to see who could name ze Southampton manager. Brucey Bonus was closest with David Copperfield, but we never did find out for sure.

MONDAY 20TH NOVEMBER
Zis English life is so odd. Isabella wanted to watch ze Panoboro because Lady Thick was dishing ze shit on big ears and ze rest of ze Royal Family. We French are republicans and cannot understand how you can all fawn and gawp at ze imbeciles who are living it up on your hard-earned money. It was certainly funny, zough, because when she was talking about how a powerful group was excluding a person, making zat person feel ugly and useless and surplus to requirements, I wondered what David Maynotgetinzeteamforzesecondseasonrunning was thinking.

WEDNESDAY 22ND NOVEMBER
A very pleasing result as we kebabed ze Coventry Shitty. Zere manager, Ron Fatkinson was as absurd as usual wearing his shell suit and sun glasses on a November evening. Denis Bogman scored a good

goal and zen we just over-ran zem. Brian McClard had his one good game of ze season and was taking ze piss out of Andy Colenotdole. I had my own brand of fun taking ze pissoir out of Richard Shawisshit. "So you got out of the First Division - but not for long you sack of shit". You should have seen Giggsy leave him on his arse with a lovely dummy. David Beckenham-by-pass scored a nifty goal as well and we all sang songs on ze coach home. Zere was even an appearance by David Maygetonzepitchfor10minuteswhenweare4-0up. Ze only shame was seeing Dion Belfast's sad face at ze final whistle. Zere was a lot of talk about Blackbum zough because of ze fight between Nora Batty and Graeme Le Sick. It was so funny. We all couldn't wait to get home and see it. Raphael had taped it for me 16 times - and it just got better and better. Graeme Le Sick certainly showed what a man's man he is with such a display of macho boxing. It will be good to see Ray Halfwit giving his usual excuses. What a pissoir display by ze so-called Champions Of England. What fine team spirit zey are showing. Even Tim Sheershit nearly had a bust-up with Colin Ugly - but even if he'd hit him in ze face, it could hardly have done any harm.

SUNDAY 26TH NOVEMBER
Raphael came in and said: Don't rush your dinner, Papa...Arsewipe vs Blackbum is ze worst game ze Premiership has ever seen!'.

MONDAY 27TH NOVEMBER
I did not enjoy zis game at all. We were missing too many of ze players to beat Forest. David Beckenhamby-pass forgot how to pass ze ball and Andy Colenotdole thought he was playing on ze wing. Ze only good thing was getting another penalty kick. Ze oafish Steve Scuttle brought me down. We were all wondering on ze coach afterwards how such an ordinary team had gone so far in Europe.

SATURDAY 2ND DECEMBER
Raphael started ze day by eating a piece of chocolate out of his Giggsy Man United advent calendar, which was only £16. However he spat ze piece out because it looked like Peter BeardotheWeirdo's head. "Let me avv a look at zis, son," I said. "No, Raphael, it's supposed to be an elephant". We played badly against ze Chelseasick and Andy Colenotdole looked no more like scoring zan Sparky. David Beckenham-by-pass saved a point with a good shot but Fergie took off Coley after a dreadful miss in front of goal. When I asked him about it afterwards he said zat he was still in a state of

shock zat he'd actually got a decent pass from Lee NotSharpeatall. He gave away ze ball for for their goal and I'm not sure who Fergie was more annoyed with after ze game. He just stood in ze middle of ze dressing room snarling: "Gobshite!...You know, Jimmy, I've still got £8 million to spend and I might do as soon as Steve Stoneageman loses two hundred pounds of fat!" .

FRIDAY 8TH DECEMBER

We avv decided zat zis year's United Christmas party should be as ze theme of Coronation Street so people have to come as different characters. It was decided zat Kiddo was ze impractical man to allocate ze roles. However, it was quite heated when he read zem out: "Number One - Brucey Bonus is Des because of his resemblance, Two - Lee NotsoSharpeatall is Steve McDonald. He's about as reliable as him and they both like the buzz scene in Manchester...". 'What can he mean?', I heard one of ze Neville Brothers asking.
"Third - Paul Schoolboys is Vicky, as they share the same revolting hair colour. Four - Bogman is Jim McDonald because you can't understand either of them. Five - Giggsy is Maxine - pretty face and spindly legs, Pally is Ken Barlow - the two most boring men in England. Brian McClard is Alf Roberts, although I'm not sure who is the fatter and Peter Struedal is Percy Sugden - because you can't shut either of them up".
'What about Monsieur Cantona?' shouted out Giggsy. "Well, he's already a film star" said Kiddo. Zen he was not joking. My new film was premiered in France zis week. My brother Joel is in it, too. I play a man who falls in love with the daughter of a man who manufactures toilets. When I told ze lads zis, Denis Bogman nearly collapsed. He still thinks I'm joking - but to show zat life is stranger zan fiction, I am not.

SATURDAY 9TH DECEMBER

A pissoir poor display against Sheffield Tuesday, It was a case of men against boys. We were just over-run. We were not helped by some terrible misses. I set up Brian McClard for a simple header in ze six-yard-box but he lumbered in with all ze grace of Mr Blobby and chucked it into ze keeper's hands with a little glanced header. Sacre fucking Bleu!, I shouted. I threw my arms down. 'I know my dear' said Isabella, even Trevor Boring said so in Match Of Ze Day. McClard is so fat, I said. I know cows have two stomachs but so does zat man sometimes. I think he's followed ze Claire Raynor fitness plan. Fergie congratulated me after ze game and in truth it was pleasing to have scored two delightful little goals, but we need something in ze team.

I think Fergie knows because I saw him leafing through ze Who's Who Of Players and stopping in ze S section. It was an odd day all round - even David Maygetinzeteamifheputs backstrainpillsinPally'stea did not make a total arse of himself. Still, at least Newcastle lost.

FRIDAY 15TH DECEMBER

Zere was a strange atmosphere at ze training ground today. We avv a big match in ze Mickey Mouse land on Sunday but nobody seems confident. After ze training session, a few of ze young lads came up to me for advice. "Just duck ze filthy gob zey spit at you". 'Ah cawm on mate', said David Beckenham-by-pass. 'Tell us!'. "If I have to pass on advice in zis life I'd tell you all to learn ze words to ze latest songs, wear comfortable underpants and smile all the time".'Oh no', said Paul Schoolboys, 'he's keeping something back'. 'Yeah, please tell us', sang the Neville Brothers in zere New Orleans style.
"Scare Bleu...well if I must. First, eat lots of bran to provide ze necessary bulk in your diet. Ze sight of Brian McLard and ze damage all zose cream cakes have done should prove ze wisdom of zat statement".
"Second - and zis was Blind Pierre Burgundy's pearl of advice - never stick anything in your ears. The tiniest bones in your bodies are inside your ears. If you mess around with your ears you could become deaf or start falling down. Leave zem as zey are". Zen zey all skulked off but I noticed zat one of ze Neville Brothers was pointing at his brother's ears.

SUNDAY 17TH DECEMBER

Great Balls of Sacha Distel, zis was Sunday Bloody Sunday. We were so bad against ze Scousers zat I thought we were Manchester Shitty in disguise. Fergie took off Andy Colenotdole who couldn't have hit Gerard Depardieu's arse with a wine bottle (and zat's something zat has been done many times). Ze coach home after ze game was silent and pretty dingy considering ze windows were covered in four tonnes of Scouse saliva.

SATURDAY 23RD DECEMBER

Did some early morning Christmas shopping with my little bears, Raphael and Josephine. Zey both got Giggsy pack lunch boxes, Giggsy shower caps and Giggsy-decorated thermal socks. We also got a Lee NotsoSharpe parachute action man - which is also designed to be dropped on every conceivable occasion.

CHRISTMAS EVE

Isabella rang me today to wish me luck on my return to Helland Road. 'Don't fret mon petite Parisian bun', I told her - speaking on Paul Nosey Parker's mobile phone, equipped with infra-red bugging and recording devices - zis is the season of goodwill to all men, of love, peace and Christmas cheer. Naturally, I got nothing but abuse from zose bitter Yorkshire puddings. All I could see all match was hordes of whippet-stinking, clog-wearing lard-arses straining to think of something to shout. Ze only sight worse zan zat was the one of Paul Nosey Parker trying to stay on his feet for more zan three seconds. I know zat I am below par at ze moment, but our team are complete dog poo. Nicky Butthead must avv thought zat he was using his arms in Charlie Chin's again, ze way his hand shot up to grab ze ball in our penalty area. Zen Andy Colenotdole scored a nifty shot on ze turn before Nosey Parker slipped on his arse again to allow zat Phoney Yeboah to beat Peter Struedal. Ze only thing redder zan Peter's nose at ze moment is Fergie's neck. It is fair to say zat his blood was boiling at ze end of ze game.

CHRISTMAS DAY

I think ze boss is less zan happy. We were not allowed to wear ze Christmas hats from our crackers and we all sat in silence watching Jurassic Park on Sky TV. When ze woman puts her arm in a big pile of dinosaur crap, he muttered under his breath: "I haven't seen that much shit since we last played the Bitter Blues". Zat evening Raphael rang me up to crack ze same old joke I must avv heard a thousand times when Victor Meldrew is on. "Now Papa, don't forget to watch One Foot In Ze Crowd - you know you starred in zat once!".

BOXING DAY

Zere was a message from ze French national coach, Army Jacket, on ze answer-phone saying zat we should meet for a drink after ze game against ze Geordies. I will definitely go because he said: 'You might like to know zat ze big ponce called David Ginandtonic will not be invited'.

WEDNESDAY 27TH DECEMBER

Zut Alors! Ze Reds were magnifique. Kevin Peegun and his Geordies may win ze league zis season but zey were taught a lesson in football tonight. Ze best part was ze fantastic goal by Andy Colenotdole. It was a sweeping move involving me and Giggsy and he hit it first time - "as sweet as a nut" as David Beckenham-by-pass says - and it flew into ze net. We could avv had a hatfull but at least Roy KeaneasMustard, who is a lot calmer since he's been sucking ze Prozac lollipops, finished zem off with a cheeky goal. Lesbian Ferdinand was all cocky in ze bar after ze game saying zat he was looking forward to grabbing the title for ze first time. Giggsy said something along ze lines of been zere and done it - but I wasn't sure if he was talking about ze Championship or Dani Bearall. Once again I marvel at Harry Enfield's versatility - doing all his comedy shows as ze loud-mouthed scally and being Newcastle's assistant manager, Terry McDimwit.

FRIDAY 29TH DECEMBER

I am close to winning my bet with Blind Papa Burgendy. I bet him zat I could get William Prunehead a game for United. 'But he is one of ze most shocking slapheads in ze whole of France', said Papa. Fergie is a bit short of ze options. Pally still has his mystery back injuries which Denis Bogman says is due to him bending over to pick up loose change in ze streets and Brucey Bonus's corset is wedged tight and has to be surgically removed. Zat means ze Prunehead will play against Queens Bend Over In Ze Park Rangers. Somehow, I don't think Prunehead and Gay Wilkins will be fighting over a comb in ze dressing room.

SATURDAY 30TH DECEMBER

Sacre Bleu! William Prunehead put on a good show and even set up Andy Colenotdole's headed goal. Ze lads were all trying to work out who ze Prune looked like. Norman Tebbit, said Kiddo. The old detective Chisholm out of Minder, said Giggsy. Alan Hansoncan was praising Prunehead to ze skies on Match Of Ze Day and Fergie says he's in ze team for Tottenham. What can I do if zis practical joke rebounds on me?

1996

MONDAY 1ST JANUARY

Great Avignon arseholes, we had our worst defeat since ze Barcelona bashing when we were thrashed at ze White Shite Lane. Prunehead exceeded even my worst expectations with his impersonation of a bloodhound with no nose. He was so far way from Steady Teddy all night, zat ze Spurs forward had time to cut his toe nails before he scored. Ze other comical highlight of ze night was Peter Streudal's impersonation of Hopalong Cassidy. He was about as fit as ze man who used to play Superman. Zen nervy Pilkington Pilchards came in goal and he didn't get near ze ball. But at least Chris Jointstrong showed zat he can play on grass. After ze game, Fergie looked shell-shocked. "I'm sorry", he said, "I'm gonna haftee bomb out Prune head. But if you've got any other bright ideas - keep em to yourself!". Lucky I didn't mention ze idea of getting Tony Coton as goalkeeping cover.

WEDNESDAY 3RD JANUARY
We were all watching ze Coronation Street when ze new Lineker and Gazza crisp advert came on TV. "Well, you know what flavour ze'll have to make for zat fat twat", said Isabella: "Ready Assaulted!".

SATURDAY 6TH JANUARY
Ze whole of one side of ze ground was full of strange speaking Sooondurland fans. Zey had Peter Peed as zere manager and he looked as fit as Percy Sugden. Lee NotsoSharpe, wearing zose big girls gold boots, was trying to take ze piss out of my haircut before ze game. "It's nice to see that you give work to the disabled", he said. But zen we were talking about Roy Keane As Mustard letting his hair grow long. "I've got it", yelled Bogman. "I know who he reminds me of - it's Bobby Ewing!". We were all laughing so much we couldn't concentrate on ze game and were lucky to get away with a 2-2 draw. Every time anyone went near Roy we hummed ze theme tune of Dallas and he was getting more and more annoyed. He got through eight Prozac lollipops at half-time. Only a certain magnifique Frenchman saved ze day with a late header.

MONDAY 8TH JANUARY
Army Jacket left a message - 'A few more like zat my little Monsieur and you're back in ze squad'.

FRIDAY 12TH JANUARY
All ze talk was about David Ginandtonic and whether he was being treated too roughly after he reacted against lee DixonofDockgreen. 'Well, I only told Bogman to kick him every other minute' joked Kiddo.

SATURDAY 13TH JANUARY
Aston Vanilla are officially ze biggest boring bastards in ze

Premiership. Zey were so camped in zere own half zat I am surprised zey didn't go ze whole hog and bring deckchairs and sandwiches. And zere manager, Brian Littlebrain, has ze worst haircut since Ivy Tilsley. I've not seen as much old matted grey hair since Great Aunt Dildomonia got savaged by a dirty sheep on a day trip to Chambres sans crack. Zere was a sombre silence in ze dressing room after ze game when Andy Colenotdole came in. He missed a header zat I think Alf Roberts could have stooped to knock in. "Don't worry son" said Fergie. "I'm sure the goals will come. All you need is a bit of support and patience and the time to get it right - so start putting the fecking ball in the net right away you great lump of blancmange or I'll spend £12 million on a new striker".

TUESDAY 16TH JANUARY
A great night out in ze NorthEast. Peter Peed was so cocky before ze game zat he was going around saying zat his team were heading for Reading. I must admit zat I felt ze same way after about 20 minutes. Paul Nosey Parker was kicking everything zat moved - apart from ze ball - and Brucey Bonus looked like he needed a crane lift to help him change direction. Zey got a predictable goal and we all trooped off expecting to see a vintage Fergie fury. Instead he was sat in a corner with his Who's Who of European Football and a highlighter pen. He seemed to be paying great attention to ze AC Milan page - zat and Manchester Shitty and Blackbum. It was all very odd. Ze second half showed us back to our best. We passed ze ball like master Casino ball handlers and pulled zem apart. Paul Schoolboys cracked a great little equaliser and zen, in ze final minute, Andy Colenotdole scored a magnifique header. We're heading for Reading he said as he passed a wizened grey haired little dwarf who was standing outside ze Sunderland dressing room.

WEDNESDAY 17TH JANUARY
Brian McClard siddled up to Giggsy and was being all matey. "Why are you being so friendly? - I haven't got any food", he said, and McLard rolled away again.

THURSDAY 18TH JANUARY
Roy Keane As Mustard had been down his pub having a few jars when a local asked him whether he was hard enough to work in a circus. When Roy asked what as, the man said as a lion tamer. He told Roy zat zere was only one dodgy lion in the whole circus but zat he would be alright if he just kept eye contact and took one step

back at a time then cracked his whip. "What if he keeps coming at me?" said Roy. Then the man said he should just take another step back, keep his eyes on the lion and crack his whip. "But don't stop looking into his eyes", he warned. Then Roy asked: "But what happens when I keep taking steps back and I end up against the bars of the cage?". "Then" said the man, "You maintain eye contact and slowly stoop to pick up a lump of shit and hurl it into his eyes". Roy said: "But how do I know there'll be a lump of shit there?". "There will be by then son, I promise", he said. Naturally, Bogman loved zis joke.

FRIDAY 19TH JANUARY
Fergie called us all together and said zat he had made a fantastic new signing. Boban? guessed Giggsy, Baggio? suggested Butthead, Stone? growled Beckenham-by-pass. Zen Tony Cotonking wandered in. A definite case of mistaken nonentity. We were all gobsmacked. Ze funny thing was zat when Kiddo handed him a cup of tea he dropped it all over ze floor. Ze words marbles and lost were mentioned one or two times.

SUNDAY 21ST JANUARY
I avv add another offer to star in a film following ze success of my latest movie, which just won a French Oscar. Giggsy accused me of being a "Luvvy" just because I avv started saying: "Oh my poor darling" all ze time.

MONDAY 22ND JANUARY
We were all agog on ze way to Upton Park reading of ze 13-year-old girl who'd married a Turkish waiter. "Christ is she ugly or what" said Lee NotsoSharpe in his usual tactful way. "She looks like Graham Smelly as a teenage girl". Ze Wets Ham fans were not so loopy as usual because zey did not have Incey-Wincey to bait - but we soon silenced zem anyway with a beautiful goal. Giggsy made Julian look like a complete Dicks before crossing for me to score from a difficult angle. After zat we just pissoired all over zem. Ze only frightening thing was seeing Iain Dowierightugly coming towards you. In ze second half ze referee Stephen Bodge was getting right on our nerves. Everytime someone moved he whipped out his yellow card. Zen Right Dicks nearly took Andy Colenotdole's head off. Zis was followed by Nicky Butthead's tackle which earned him ze Red Card. Andy went, as zey say, off his trolley. He was out of his pram. He was climbing ze walls and going ape shit. Step forward Saint Eric. Ze Mother Theresa of ze Premiership. 'Non!, Non!', I shouted as I

grabbed Andy's arm, 'Violence is not ze answer!...remember ze pen is mightier zan ze sword'. "He's gone bonkers", I heard Brucey Bonus say, "I think I preferred it when he was kicking people". We survived with 10 men and afterwards Kiddo said: "Blessed are the peacemakers". Giggsy called me Goody Two Shoes and David Beckenham-bypass asked me how I kept my cool now. "No problem", I told him, "Since I read Claire Raynor's pamphlet, 'How to control your temper and achieve multiple orgasms' my life has never been ze same!". Sometimes I think zat boy believes everything I say.

TUESDAY 23RD JANUARY

All ze lads went to see Pimply Red at ze Nylonex. Afterwards zere was a big party. A man with tight pants and leather trousers tried to gate crash saying zat he was a close friend of Lee NowquiteSharp - but surely he doesn't mix with anyone like zat? We were all getting drunk and guessing ze seven words zat Princess Di said to upset Lady Twiggy Burke. I think zat she really said: "So sorry to hear you support Leeds". Now zat is insulting!

FRIDAY 26TH JANUARY

Zere is a great mystery to be solved. Everytime I buy some chocolate buttons for Josephine zey are pinched from my jacket in ze changing room. I did suspect Brian McLard but he never eats anything zat small.

SATURDAY 27TH JANUARY

Off to ze Elm Park to play on a surface zat was as rutted and bumpy as Stephen Hendry's face. Ze Reading fans were giving me a bit of abuse but ze whole ground was silent after Giggsy scored. At half-time ze dressing rooms were so cramped zat Kiddo had to wait in ze ladies lavatory - Uri Geller was lurking about, bending toilet rolls. After half-time Paul Nosey Parker came on. Surprise, surprise, he was booked - zis time after 45 seconds. Zen he tried to cross a ball and it flew into ze net. 'What a bloody goal - beat that' he told Roy Keane As Mustard. 'Yeah, I remember your last goal - for Germany in the World Cup semi-Final!'. Zen I set up Brucey Bonus for an open goal - and he managed to get it over ze bar from 3 yards. Zen I went over to take a throw in and ze Reading fans started chucking coins. What a disgrace - ze most zey could manage was a 10pence piece. Zen zey chucked a banana on to ze pitch and I threw it onto ze side. Ze referee was by my side and he was upset - I think he wanted it for his tea.

Later on when I scored I pointed to my ears. People thought I was taking ze pissoir out of ze Reading retards - but ze Neville Brothers and Beckenham-by-pass know what I mean when I point to an ear!

SUNDAY 28TH JANUARY
We avv got senttoCoventry or Manchester Shitty at home in ze draw!

SATURDAY 3RD FEBRUARY
Ned Belly, zat famous Australian outlaw and minder, was all knees-a-wobbly before ze trip to Shellsuit Park, because zere had been reports zat Dismal Palace supporters were going to turn up and try to cause trouble. "Zat is not something to worry about", I told him. "Ze last thing you can get zem to do is go through ze turnstiles here in big numbers". Ze game was a let-down and we won quite easily. It was nice getting some in ze onion bag again, particularly ze dinky little header from David Beckenham-by-pass's clever chip. Ze dons really are a bag of shite but we were all jolly enough on ze coach home. Brucey Bonus has even started telling jokes about old age, something I believe ze psychobabblers call a "defence mechanism". 'Nah', shouted ze Neville brothers. 'He's no expert on anything to do with the defence!'. Anyway, Brucey Bonus got a big laugh when he said zere was an old married couple on a day outing. She was 60 and he was 75. They went out into the Cheshire countryside: 'Let's go back to that field dear, you know, the place we first did it!'.
"Did what, my dear?" said the husband.
'You know, sealed our love. Don't you remember, it was here - by this fence. You leaned on the fence, held me in your arms and made passionate love'.
"I'm sorry, my love" said the husband, "I just don't remember".
The wife led him up to the fence and pulled down his trousers. 'Look, my dear, let's do it here again, one more time and it might jog your memory'. They made wild love for an hour and when it was over the wife yelled: 'That was fantastic - even better than the first time all those years ago...'. "Yes, dear", said the old man, "But the fence wasn't electrified in those days!".
Everyone laughed a lot, especially Roy Keane As Mustard after ze joke was explained to him.

SATURDAY 10TH FEBRUARY
Ze Reds gave real stick to Alan Shearenvy, ze man with a worst record for England zan Paul Mariner. We beat zem easily, but it is a disgrace to think zat zey are ze Champions - zey are not fit to defend

zat crown. Zere bitterness is so evident zat Shearenvy even had a kick at Peter Streudal. But what a surprise, he only got ze yellow card. Ze funny thing was zat back in ze dressing room, Fergie kept saying: "och, he's na that bad is our Alan".

FRIDAY 16TH FEBRUARY

All ze lads were laughing about ze Keith Gulliblespie and his wild betting sprees. Everyone it seemed had won silly money off him. Lee LookingmoreSharpe won ze competition, zough, when he said zat he had won £250 off him betting zat United would win ze 1994 FA Cup Final. 'What was so easy about zat?', said Pally. "Well, we were 4-0 up at the time", said Lee LookingmoreSharpe.

SUNDAY 18TH FEBRUARY

At last, another chance to pissoir off ze Manchester Shitty. Ze funniest thing about ze whole match was zat zey had a tantalising bit of false hope for 20 minutes zat was - as ever with zat side - blown into thin air. Zey had so many Germans playing for zem zat it inspired all ze old Franco suspicions of zose war-loving Nazi arsewipes. But surely zere has been no more ludicrous Kraut zan ze full back Twatzeck. I wound him up like a clock. "I can't believe zat of 100,000 sperm, you were ze fastest!", I said to him. Zen at a corner, I said: "Your mother should have kept the stork and thrown you away". At zat point he tried to strangle me right in front of ze referee - a little bald man with a squinty eye zat I recall from somewhere but couldn't quite place. All ze Shitty players, including ze drunk's son, ze useless lanky Irishman, and Georgi Kinkywithlads, surrounded ze official but to no avail. Wham! In went ze spot kick. Ze second half was pissoir easy, except for ze piercing sound of Alan Balls-Up whining from ze touch line. Even zen ze Bitter Blues, who last won a trophy when Percy Sugden was young, were gloating thinking zat zey had a draw. But just when zey were giving ze Munich signals, Lee LookingmoreSharpe volleyed home ze winner. Just to see zose twisted, embittered faces was joy enough. After ze game, zey were moaning moaning about ze referee and ze penalty decision. "Who was zat man?" , I asked Kiddo. 'He was the one who sent you off for the Richard Shawisshit incident'. "He looked to me like a man with a guiltyconscience - maybe zat explains ze penalty!". Poor old Manchester Shitty. Perhaps zey should ask Vera Duckworth to hold a seance to bring to life the days they once won a trophy. What is it ze Reds sing: "20 years and won fuck all, City is our name". Well, zere will certainly be a 21st party next year.

TUESDAY 20TH FEBRUARY

In training all ze lads were talking about ze Jarvis cockup and ze Brit awards. I liked what his Dad said about it being a brave man to show his arse in the proximity of Michael Jackson. Steve Brucey Bonus was all in a buoyant mood, because he'd had a big bet on Wets Ham beating ze Newcastle. He was so jolly, we even allowed him to tell another of his old age jokes. "Well. This old man was preparing for his eightieth birthday and his family thought they'd give him one last treat and send in a high class call girl. They hired the woman and she said: 'What do I have to do?'. "Just go in and tell him you're going to give him some super sex - but speak up because the poor old chap is a bit hard of hearing". Anyway, the woman goes into the room where the old man is and takes off her coat. "I've come to offer you super sex" she says. "I'll have the soup!" says the old man. We all laughed at zat - but not half as loudly as we laughed when Tony Pottee scored ze second against ze Geordies.

THURSDAY 22ND FEBRUARY

"Hey, hey everyone..." shouted Bogman Irwin when he came into ze training ground canteen, "did anyone see Bjork doing her Roy KeaneasMustard impression yesterday?".

SATURDAY 24TH FEBRUARY

Who would have believed zat Manchester Shitty would have been able to do us a favour and nick a point off ze Geordies - and doesn't zat Faustino Asprinhead look a calm model professional. Only one elbow and one nutting per match. Actually, I would like to avv put down zat he was a gun-toting, porn-star dating, bus vandalising dodgy South American - but ze Daily Mail has already said all of zat, so nobody will be shocked!

SUNDAY 25TH FEBRUARY

Now ze title race is firmly back on after we beat ze Michael Bolton 6-0. Zey gave a wonderful performance of Men Defending Badly. Ze match was all done and dusted within ze first 15 minutes. Giggsy did one of his wonderful littlebits of cheek and it was a pity zat he didn't score. Zen Brucey Bonus scored his first goal since last March. He wanted to tell another of his jokes at half-time but Fergie banned him, threatening to open up ze big canvas trunk in ze corner of ze dressing room. "What's in zere?", asked one of ze Neville Brothers. "Paul   Nosey   Parker   and

DavidMaynotgetinzeteamforzesecondseasonrunning", said Fergie. Ze second half was so boring zat I waved to come off ze field pretending to have a slight muscle pull. Giggsy copied me about two minutes later. Zen ze floodgates opened and Paul Schoolboys, Andy Colenotdole and Nicky Butthead finished off ze Bolton. Zey are so shit it is no surprise zat zey are bottom of ze Premiership. I would not have believed zat zere was a slower, fatter and more awkward forward zan Brian Deane if I had not seen Phil de Freitas playing. After ze game zere was so mighty pissoir-taking of Roy KeaneasMustard, who gave one of his inimitable interviews to Sky TV. He said twice zat we had won five nil. "What's the matter?" said David Beckenham-by-pass, "Do you have trouble counting past the number of fingers on your hand?". Well, even he can figure out zat we are only four points behind ze leaders now. I wonder if Terry McDimwit is going round St James Park shouting: "Calm down, calm down".

TUESDAY 27TH FEBRUARY
All ze papers are now saying zat Fergie is going to bid £4million for some Portuguese bloke who plays in Italy after we lost ze Mark Fish to Lazio. I didn't want him to stay in any case. I told him my famous sardine joke eight times and he didn't get it once. Zat is ze thing about ze South Africans, ze French humour is too subtle for zem. Oh well, ze crunch time is coming soon.

FRIDAY 1ST MARCH
Zis is ze month where ze title race will really hot up. Some of ze lads were getting a bit keyed up about Monday's game but zen Brucey Bonus made us all laugh by suggesting a team trip to ze zoo: "David Maynotgetinzeteamforzesecondseasonrunning will be less conspicuous!".

SATURDAY 2ND MARCH
Old Braindead Clough was having his mouth-off day again about ze Championship. At least his wife has a sobering effect - she hides ze bottle. You just have to gin and bear it with him. Football criticism is like an airport - acceptable as long as it's not in my direction.

SUNDAY 3RD MARCH
Fergie came up and asked me to help because some of ze lads were getting a case of ze jittery-wittery before ze big game at St James Park. First of all I lightened ze atmosphere by telling my joke. 'Why is it all ze football people who come here from abroad have ze

same sort of nickname. Well Terry Venables was El Tel and now zere is Faustino Asprinhead who is El Bow'. Zey all laughed. Zen ze Neville Brothers, David Beckenham-by-pass, Nicky Butthead, Paul Schoolboys and Giggsy sat in a ring while we all sang nursery rhymes zat Raphael used to like. Zere favourite was: 'Two little monkeys fighting in bed, One fell out and banged his head, The other rang the Doctor, And the Doctor said: "Zat's what you get for fighting in bed!" Everyone laughed a lot, especially Roy Keane As Mustard after ze joke was explained to him.

MONDAY 4TH MARCH

It is ze big test for Kevin Peegun and his men. If zey win ze title is virtually theirs. If not zey may crack up like Lady Diane. Zey were a bit cocky before ze kick-off. Lesbian Ferdinand started saying he'd make mincemeat of ze Neville Brothers. First of all Giggsy went past and said: "So, she's upsetting your form now is she?", which made him grimace, zen I walked up and said: "Do not be so confident, Lesbian. Remember ze old motto of Blind Papa Burgundy: 'Do not insult the mother alligator until you have crossed the river". I heard him say: "What the fuck's he on about?", which annoyed Denis Bogman, who said: 'I think, roughly translated, it means we're gonna do you!' Just as we were going out I noticed Keith Gullible filling out a lot of pink slips with 'Ginola first to score' on zem. Raphael has told me to score because he's had a fiver on me as first to score. I think I will oblige. We were just a tiny bit lucky in ze first half but at half-time we knew we'd win. Zey had burnt zere boots ('Boats' Isabella has just shouted). Mini Neville did a wonderful cross and I smashed in a volley. Ze Geordies were a sick as old Flaubert's parrot. Terry McDimwit was going round and round ze tunnel area saying: "Calm down, calm down!'. At least his hair will never go out of style. It will look ridiculous year after year.

MONDAY 11TH MARCH

Raphael shouted out as I was leaving: "First to score, Dad please, I'm saving up for ze big Subbuteo set". Ze Southampton were determined but zey were let down by having fat Matthew Le Pissier in ze midfield. He's certainly put on weight. He has so many chins now, you'd need a bookmark to find his mouth. I scored again but only after zey had had a goal disallowed for ze most disgraceful push with an index finger I've ever seen. Ze force with which Neil Shitterley knocked over Lee NotsoSharpe would have been enough to push over a piece of paper. Well, we're into ze Semi-finals again. Zis winning lark is getting a bit dull.

WEDNESDAY 13TH MARCH

Ze worst day since I came to England. A mad gunman killed all ze children in Dunblane. I could not stop hugging Raphael and Josephine. What a crazed world zis can be.

SATURDAY 16TH MARCH

Zere was a minute's silence before ze QPR game which everyone observed impeccably. It was a frustrating game. We should avv been four up after 10 minutes. Andy Colenotgoal is in a rich vein of goalscoring form. Not. At half-time Fergie was just walking round tutting. I thought he was going to hurl a plate of sandwiches like zat man at Grimsby. 'Don't worry' said Brucey Bonus, "he did that a few seasons ago and Brian McCLard caught them all in his mouth!' In ze second half zey brought on Andrew Impey, I think he used to be with a band called The Men They Couldn't Hang. He certainly has no neck. Zen Bogman scored an own goal. Zey kept time wasting and I kept reminding ze referee zey were time wasting. In ze end he added on 23 minutes which was just enough time for me to score an equaliser from a great Giggsy cross. In all ze papers, zough, zey described it as Cantona, 90 minutes! I think we were lucky to get a point especially with ze two useless M's in ze team. Still it puts us top of ze league for ze first time in six months. On ze coach home zere was a battle over what was on ze telly on ze coach. Kiddo wanted Barrymore but I said: "Zats all England needs, another Queen who can't dress". Zere was a heated row until finally Fergie had ze last say and put on A History Of Manchester Shitty to give us all a big laugh.

SUNDAY 17TH MARCH

Spent all day practising ze trumpet. It is my new hobby. Heard zat Frank Bruno lost to Tyson. Bruno couldn't go three rounds with a revolving door.

MONDAY 18TH MARCH

Newcastle went top again by beating Wets Ham - but zen if Mad Dog Sealey was zere best player, zat says it all. He hadn't played since 1961. I spent the evening watching ze Marx Brothers, A Day At Ze Races. I love ze bit where Groucho says: "Marry me and I'll never look at another horse".

WEDNESDAY 20TH MARCH

Ze familiar sound as I left ze house: "First to score, papa". It was a good night. Being marked by Andy Linighan was like being trailed by two tonnes of condemned veal. We had so many chances it was embarrassing. Eventually I thought I'd outdo Phoney Yeboah. I scored a magnificent goal. Fergie described me as being like a ballet dancer - but I would never wear zose tights!

FRIDAY 22ND MARCH

We spent a lot of time in training on finishing. It was odd but while Paul Schoolboys seemed to score from every angle and distance, poor Andy Colenotgoal could not get ze ball in ze net. Kiddo said to Brucey Bonus: "Well, don't worry - because he's putting in ze effort, he's doing ze work of two men". "Yeah - Laurel & Hardy!", said David Beckenham-by-pass.

SATURDAY 23RD MARCH

What a great afternoon. Listened to Newcastle get beaten at Arsewipe, ze Mickey Mousers lost at Forest and Manchester Shitty were beaten at Wets Ham. Alan Balls-Up was squeaking and moaning again, but as Blind Uncle Pierre once told me: "Never trust a little man. His brains are too near his arse". Zat night I saw Paul Nosey Parker eating another beefburger. I for one am sure zat mad cow disease can get into ze human chain.

SUNDAY 24TH MARCH

What is happening - another great day! We were lucky to beat ze Tottenham. Zey were making a song and dance about Frank Skinner-lookalike Andy Sinton avving a corner. But don't zey know ze new FIFA rule - zat it has to come off a United player twice! I scored another goal, my fifth in successive games, which should keep me in Raphael's good books. He's made a fortune recently. Not so Merry Francis was whining about ze referee. "Oh no, he is consistently good", I said..."Remember when he sent off Henning Berk for tripping Lee NotsoSharpe". We are now three points clear and ze Geordies must be pissoiring in zere pants. Oh yes - and Leeds lost a Final playing absolute merde. I wonder if I should leave a message on Sergeant Wilko's ansaphone thanking him again for letting me go. Ze only disappointing thing was zat zere was no more News Of Ze Screws stories about Lee NotsoSharpe's sexual peculiarities.

MONDAY 25TH MARCH

Ze Sky Tv was entertaining tonight - Fat Ron exploded when he was being interviewed. Why is it zat he still looks like a victim of Forceps delivery.

TUESDAY 26TH MARCH

A night out at ze flicks. Fergie has organised a charity showing of a John Revolting film in Bury. I took Isabella and dressed up in ze dinner jacket. Of course it was all a bit of ze old hat to an experienced luvvy like me. I think I was getting on Brian McClard's nerves by saying: "Great balls of Sacha Distel - what is ze director doing in zis scene". Needless to say zere were some oily photographers from ze Scum Newspaper zere, trying to photograph Giggsy with his girlfriend. When we were introduced Giggsy said her name was Davinia. 'Zat is sweet', said my wife, but zen Steve Brucey Bonus whispered: "Her real name is Beryl, but Ryan and Davinia sounds a bit more yuppified". After ze film we were having a drink and Fergie started going on again about how he loved ze Theatre and ze West End musical premieres. Funnily enough, ze bar emptied within seconds again. As I was leaving Brian McClard came over and said: "I passed by your house yesterday", and I just said: 'Thankyou!'.

WEDNESDAY 27TH MARCH

More slagging off in ze papers. Yesterday it was Carlton Palmtree with ze Leeds players. He has every attribute of a dog except loyalty. Today it was Lesbian Ferdinand on Faustino Asprinhead. Zere is nothing like great team spirit...and zis is definitely nothing like it.

SATURDAY 30TH MARCH

All ze lads were getting keyed up for ze match. I listened to my Charles Aznovoice tape and some of ze young lads came in to watch Raphael's copy of ze Jungle Book. Fergie passed me a note at dinner saying zat Steve Brucey Bonus would not be fit for ze Semi-Final. Some people say Brucey Bonus is still as fit as a fiddle but I think he looks more like a cello. With Bogman and Pally also out zis means David Maygetinzeteamifwe'reallinjured is in. He came over and said all cockily: "I'll show you a thing or two about defending tomorrow". So we bet £100 zat I would make more goalline clearances zan him.

SUNDAY 31ST MARCH

All ze Chelseasick players were very cock-a-leeky soup before ze game. I saw Sparky and said was it because Glenn Won-Hoddall gave brilliant team-talks. He said no - zey were awful. He got told off for laughing at one when ze Chelseasick manager said: "Zere will be no cliches in my talk. I hate cliches. I avoid them like the plague".

Ze game itself was a very exciting one. David Beckenham-by-pass was overjoyed to be in ze team - and he hit ze post with a great effort. But zey took ze lead when Sparky did his impression of a human bulldozer to set up Ruud Topullitinpublic for an easy header. It still does not seem right seeing Sparky in ze wrong colours. Zen just before half-time I hit ze post with a magnifique shot. During half-time Fergie was very calm, he just said: "You are better zan zis shower of shit - go out and prove it!" We pissoired ze second half, made easier by Terry Phelansick doing his impression of Hopalong Cassidy. I thought zat I must make a goal for Andy Colenotdole - so I headed it within three millimetres of ze net - and even he couldn't miss from zat range. Ze pitch was like a rotten old bread pudding - but David Beckenham-by-pass kept his nerve to steer home ze winner. Wemberley! Wemberley! Zere was just time to win ze bet by heading of ze line from Frank Spencer's volley. Peter Streudal nearly collapsed when he saw who it was on ze line. As I was going off I said to David Maygetinzeteamifwe'reallinjured: "Zat's £100 please". Afterwards, Brucey Bonus was all grinning, even zough he hadn't played, and asked if I'd seen Roy KeaneasMustard give Dennis UnWise a slap on ze head. I thought I heard a sound of wood, I said. Zen on ze coach, Kiddo told us zat zere was no beef on ze menu for a while. "What's the difference between a beef sausage and Dennis Unwise's head?", said Giggsy. "Don't Know!" we shouted..."There's brains in ze sausage" said Giggsy. We all laughed. Zere was no champagne on ze coach home, zough, because some plonker had dropped it. Ze only Red not happy was Raphael, who demanded to know how I could have let a scruffy old Dutchman be first to score.

TUESDAY 2ND APRIL
All ze papers are saying zat Fergie wants to buy some George Michael lookalike called George Donnis kebab.

WEDNESDAY 3RD APRIL
A great game on Sky, if only to see Steve Brucey Bonus try not to wet himself at ze end when Stan Cauliflower broke ze Geordies hearts. Football can certainly be a cruel game. I still think zat Kevin Peegun made a ricket buying zat Colombian. He's all fur coat and no knickers. Oops! Isabella will give me a kick if she reads zat!

C'mon Boyz give me a Break I'm getting zer right Royal Hump having to rescue you each WEEK!
Eric
Help
Doodoodoo" doo
Eric
Eric
Eric
Eric
7th

SATURDAY 6TH APRIL

I almost felt sorry for Manchester Shitty fans, when zey went to 2-2 you just knew zat ze carpet would be whipped from under their feet again. Raphael was a picture of delight when I got home, he's now running an under 10s syndicate on Papa being first to score. A great win.

MONDAY 8TH APRIL

Before ze game Fergie told us zat if we won Newcastle would bottle it tonight. However we were all upset by ze terrible injury to David Busst's leg. Peter Streudal said ze sight of ze blood turned his stomach. Zut alors! I could not believe some of the chances that went begging. I think we were all put off by ze constant chomp, chomp, chomp of Fat Ron and his chewing gum. At half-time ze boss reminded us zat zis was David Maygetinzeteamifwe'reallinjured's twelfth game of the season, which meant he now qualified for a championship medal. 'Go out and prove what a mad world it is' - for some reason old carrot head took this as a compliment. I scored ze winner again, and people wanted to know why I delayed for a split second before shooting past Steve Uglygit - it was just to wind up Raphael! Fergie came up to me afterwards and said: 'Saint Eric bless you, you've done it again. You're leading us to another title'. Zat is not my ultimate challenge I thought, zat is Roy Keane As Mustard's temper. In ze press conference Fergie called me 'ooh ahh'...make a note to call him Rab C.Nesbit next time I give an interview. Watched ze Newcastle game, and Isabella came in when zere was seven minutes left. She looked at me in amazement and said why are you taking ze wrapper off ze top of ze champagne bottle. I said: 'Newcastle always save the best entertainment for the last five minutes'. I raised a glass once again to David Beresford. It's time to buy more Brasso...

SATURDAY 13TH APRIL

Down to ze Dell for ze Southampton game. We were a complete bucket of merde. Andy Colenotgoal is going to ze dogs faster zan a load of fleas. He looked about as likely to score as Francis Benali - who has never put ze ball in ze Onion bags for ze Saints. At half-time Fergie was hopping mad and he screamed at us: "What ze ham and eggs was going wrong".' It is ze grey strips' said Giggsy - 'We can't see each other'. I could not believe it when he fell for zat. I thought it was because we were crap and Peter Streudal kept dropping ze ball. Zen Paul Schoolboys said: "Yeah, and Andy says he can

never see those big white poles they put at each end of the pitch".
He is now keeping a list of all the Premiership players who have
scored more times than Andy Colenotgoal - and funnily enough he
keeps leaving it on Fergie's seat. Ze second half was not much better - but at least Giggsy managed to put one past Dave 'fingers and
thumbs' Beasant. Letting him keep a clean sheet would have been
truly embarrassing. We thought Fergie would be Rab C Nesbitt like
on ze coach home but he just said: "What's the difference between
an egg and a good fart" - "You can't beat a good fart!...Don't
worry lads. Life could be worse. You could look like Beardo the
Weirdo".

SUNDAY 14TH APRIL

I could not face listening to ze radio zis afternoon. Gary Lineker and
Jimmy Chinbag Hill were on it and when zey get to talking it's always
an I for an I. Kevin Peegun's side won so I suppose ze suspense will
go on. All ze lads were off to play golf and when Isabella asked if I
was going I said 'Non!'. But she said zat all women would like Greg
Norman. 'Why, my petite pois?'. "We'd all like a man who stays on
top for 3 days and still comes second!".

WEDNESDAY 17TH APRIL

A game against ze Sergeant Wilko's crappy army. As usual trying to
stop Manchester United winning something was more important to
zem zan performing in zere own Cup Final. We did not play well but
all I could see for ze first half hour was Carlton Plonker's big legs flapping about like a windmill. Zen when Andy Colenotgoal tried to
score from ze narrowest angle in history. I lost my temper and
banged ze inside of ze net. Later on he asked me what all zat string
was for. Finally Roy Keane As Mustard stepped in with a great goal.
In ze dressing room afterwards we were all really happy. Zen Brucey
Bonus said zat he had heard ze story of a Leeds man who had gone
to live in ze Cheshire countryside. After a week he went to ze doctor
and said: "Doctor, I'm not feeling myself. I keep getting chills and
feeling feverish. I'm definitely not myself". The Doctor said: "Go
home and stick your head in a bucket of shit three times a day - and
make sure you inhale". Three weeks later the man from Leeds
returned to the Doctor and said: "Doc, that was great. I feel just fine
again. What was wrong with me?" "You were homesick" said ze
Doctor. We all pissoired ourselves laughing. Zen Fergie went out of
the door and said: "If you think that's funny - just see the reaction I'll
get from what I'll say next - it will rattle a few babies out of zere

prams!".

In ze players bar afterwards, ze Leeds players were all pleased because zey had given us such a tough game. "Yeah, it was really worth it, wasn't it? said Brian McClard as he tucked into another pie. "I mean, at the end of this you have another defeat and no points. It's better than trying in the Coca-Cola Cup Final. I mean, in that game all that's on offer is a major trophy and a place in Europe. Well, must be going, we've got a Double to play for!". All you could see were a row of clenched mouths.

SUNDAY 21ST APRIL

Raphael came running in with a huge grin, shouting: "Papa, Papa we avv both done so well". I asked him what he meant. 'Well, you've won ze Footballer Of Ze Year Award from zose scruffy old twats in trench coats and I won £250 on my win double...I had you to be Player Of Ze Year and Will Carling and his wife to split up!'. Ze phone did not stop ringing but I did not answer. I will avv to think up something to say about ze scavenger seagulls. I bet a load only voted for me so zey would avv something controversial to write about.

SATURDAY 27TH APRIL

Fergie did not look nervous at all as we prepared to face ze Forest. 'Remember, this is a team that lost heavily to Blackburn' was all he said in the team talk. That put us all at rest. For some reason Paul Schoolboys was looking really chirpy and he was even allowed to stay up to see Stars In Their Eyes. 'Why do you keep watching that?' Pally asked him. 'I'm waiting to see Peter Streudal do his Pavarotti impression'. Just because he's now 16 stone, ze young ones are all taking ze mickey. "Don't mention music to Peter for Christ sake" said Nicky Butthead. "Or we'll hear about his single in Denmark and his recording studio for the next eight hours again".

SUNDAY 28TH APRIL

Great Balls of Sacha Distel, what a fantastic result for ze Reds - but ze big talking point was zat ze Boss finally add enough of Andy Colenotgoal. I must say zat Paul Schoolboys reaction was a little strange - he ran up to Andy singing: "I'm the King of the Castle and you're a dirty rascal!" Zen we all had a bet on first to score. Keith Gullible faxed his through from Newcastle and true to ze formbook, he had £50 on Andy being ze first to score. Ze first 40 minutes were very frustrating. Steve Stoneageman was plodding about on ze right wing and our best player was David MaygetinzeteamwhenBrucehasabloatedhernia. Ze best chance fell to Lee NotatallSharpe, who proved once again zat he could not hit a cow's arse with a banjo. It was lucky zat ze Forest add zat Jason AbsolutelyLEEawful in zere team. People sing zat he has a pineapple on his head but he plays as if he has one stuck in his boot. But once Giggsy broke down ze wing and crossed for Paul Schoolboys to score I knew zat we would pissoir it - and I knew zat Raphael would avv something to say to me later on. Two minutes later David Beckenham-by-pass took a free kick zat United fan Mark Crosseyed helpfully punched right into my path. So as not to make it seem too easy I played a perfect crossfield volleyed pass on to David's head. Wham. Deux-nil. After ze break, we mullahed zem. Beckenham-by-pass scored a lovely goal, zen Giggsy scored with a shot zat was slow enough to avv won a game of croquet. Zen, right at ze whistle-blower, I volleyed ze fifth. Stick zat in your pipe Kevin Peegun and smoke it. Just to show zat I am a breakdancing dude with ze best of zem I did Blind Papa Burgendy's famous Toulon twirl as I threw myself to ze ground.

MONDAY 29TH APRIL

Sacre Bleu - I'm not sure who has ze maddest bulging eyes after tonight. Steve McDonald or Kevin Peegun. I could not believe ze Geordie boss, he had been reeled in like a dumb flapping salmon by ze Fergie tricks. I thought zat he was going to burst into tears as he shouted and jabbed his finger around saying: "I really really hope we beat them, I do. Please let us win the title, please, pretty please". I think zat at ze back of his mind might just be ze worry zat people might point ze finger at ze man who blew a 12 point lead and bought ze biggest disruption since John Redwood joined Major's cabinet.

TUESDAY 30TH APRIL

Isabella said zat zere was no real news today, just ze usual stories about low-life people in courts in Saaaarf London.

WEDNESDAY 1ST MAY

I fear zat ze news of Baby Cantona 3 may be about to leak out. Raphael has been ringing ze Scum newspaper desk again asking for £3000. Ze lads were all joking about my mask at Madame Tussauds. Zen Paul Nosey Parker said: "But they haven't got one for Roy Keane As Mustard yet". 'No - zat's in ze Blackpool Hall of Horror' joked

Bogman Irwin.

THURSDAY 2ND MAY

Who says zat ze life isn't stranger zan fiction. Ze Matthew Simpleton leapt over ze seats to attack ze Prosecutor after being found guilty of threatening behaviour. I hope ze Judge said: "It's an early sentence for you, Sir!". As a Palace fan at least he'll know what's it's like to be told he's going down. He'll be playing all his games behind closed doors for a while. Ze funniest thing was him shouting: "I'll swear on ze Bible I'm innocent". We all know, he'll swear on anything. Later on Giggsy rang up and said: "Have you heard about the agoraphobic hard man. He'd say to people: 'Come inside and say that". As usual ze Geordies saved another fuck up for ze end of ze match against Forest. Isabella came in and asked how it was going and I said a bloke called Ian Moan had equalised. 'Moan - isn't he the Newcastle manager?' she asked. Perhaps Newcastle should be sponsored by Kleenex. And Leeds showed zey add found ze consistency Sergeant Wilko wanted - losing to Spurs meant nine defeats from 10 matches. Oh well, on to ze Middlesbrough...and only a point to get. It's going to be a Super Sunday - get ze champagne on ice.

SUNDAY 5TH MAY

Championees! Championees! What a tremendous day for ze Reds. It started with a bit of a boost for everyone with ze news zat Branco was playing for zem. I avv not seen such a tub of lard wobbling about since Alf Roberts tried to run down Coronation Street.
All ze Crying in zere Newcastlebrownale fans were hoping for a slip up, but we won it down by ze Riverside and it was a bit of a stroll. Sacre Bleu, zough. After ze first goal I think we all agreed zat it was a case of David Maybewewereallwrongabouthim playing a superb game...maybe now I will believe in ze powers of hypnosis. What a shame the team he supports went down today as well! At half-time we heard zat Spurs were drawing 0-0 at St James's and after Fergie had dolled out milk and rusks to all ze United kiddiwinks, he just said: "Go out and enjoy it - and if you muck this one up I'll sack the lot of you". Ze second half couldn't avv been better. Andy Colenotdole scored a goal with his first touch, which was a surprise because we didn't know he add one. Zen Giggsy fired in ze third. "Yeah, but it's only Gary Welshrabbit he beat" said Pally. We all celebrated on ze pitch and by ze time we got indoors, Kiddo had switched on ze telly. "Why are you putting Sky 2 on?" said Brucey. 'I wanna see the Geordies weeping again' he said and we all laughed. I'm sure

somebody will still have to explain to Terry McDimwit zat he can't actually win ze title now. Zen Fergie sent Sparky a fax saying: "Ask all your team-mates: What's it like to see a team in blue win something!" Zere was a lot of champagne drunk zat night. We avv add a brilliant run and pissoired ze Championship. Even Martin Deadwood was smiling, but zen again, he did avv a calculator in his hand at ze time.

MONDAY 6TH MAY
Kiddo wanted to know why we cancelled ze open bus trip to Manchester, but zen Fergie said zat he couldn't be bothered to do it twice and it would avv to wait until after ze Cup Final. Everyone is in a confident mood and zere was even time for a round of: "Name Paul Nosey Parker's last game?". Lee NotsoSharpe was ze furthest out as he couldn't remember him playing since 1991.

TUESDAY 7TH MAY
Did an interview with Des Lemon for ze BBC1. I talked to him about my family and how it is not true zat I am arrogant. 'But you said you thought you could beat a team on your own' said Nicky Butthead. 'I was thinking of Leeds at ze time' I told him.

WEDNESDAY 8TH MAY
I think ze Boss is going to leave Steve Brucey Bonus out of ze team. Zat is cruel but football is a game for ze under fifties zese days.

THURSDAY 9TH MAY
Fergie made me go to ze Royal Lancaster Hotel to pick up ze Seagullshits Award of Ze Player Of Ze Year. Fergie's little mate from ze Male On Funday, Bob Crass, was zere - but so were 600 of ze football flotsam. I add got Denis Bogman to write my speech and, surprise, surprise, it was all about toilets. Fortunately I wasn't listening while I read it out. Zen, before I needed defumigating, I left ze room, leaving behind ze crappy little statuette and some very fat red-faced men eating some very big portions of humble pie.

FRIDAY 10TH MAY
We were all stunned by ze sight of ze Liverpool players in zere crappy cream suits. Zey all looked like seedy Michael Caine in Dirty Rotten Scoundrels. Giggsy said: "With that lack of taste, one of them will probably turn up in white boots tomorrow".

SATURDAY 11TH MAY

I am ze first Frenchman to lift ze Cup. Raphael rang me in ze morning and before he could say it I said: "Oui. I know, first to score!". 'Non, Papa. I am not making enough zat way. It has to be first to score in ze last five minutes'. "Okay", I said, "But you'll be wanting it to deflect off Rushey's big nose next". Roy was as Keane As Mustard and he just swallowed up ze Liverpool midfield. John Barnes was as conspicuous as anyone can be in ballet dancer's shoes. Poor Andy Colenotgoal was a substitute waiting to happen and ze Junior Neville will definitely get ze lower level of ze bunkbed after keeping his brother out of ze team. Ze oddest thing in ze first half was hearing Rushey say from ze bench to a linesman: "Itch my nose please, mate...you're nearer to it than I am!". Zen, in the 85th minute I put an end to ze boredom by rifling in ze goal. Sacre Bleu. I add won ze Cup for ze Reds. On ze way up ze steps ze Scummy Scousers showed zere true worth again but once again zey didn't get within spitting distance of ze Cup. One yob even tried to throw a punch at Fergie but he said he thought it was a typical Scouser trying to steal his wallet.

SUNDAY 12TH MAY

Great balls of Sacha Distel! Zere were a few mighty sore heads around zis morning. 'For Christ's sake' Fergie said at breakfast. 'If you mention the word holiday one more time Mr Frenchman, you can bloody well go to Inter Milan!' Later we went on ze bus tour of Manchester. Ze people loved it. Well, after all, it's not every year you win ze double...it's every other year. Well, as ze Star Trekkies say, now it's Europe...ze final frontier.

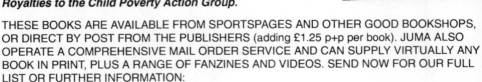